Poverty and Mental Retardation

Poverty and Mental Retardation:

A Causal Relationship

by RODGER L. HURLEY

VINTAGE BOOKS

A DIVISION OF RANDOM HOUSE

New York

Acknowledgment is gratefully extended to the following
for permission to reprint:

Basic Books, Inc.: From MENTAL SUBNORMALITY,
by Richard L. Masland, Seymour B. Sarason, and
Thomas Gladwin, 1958.
Beacon Press: From IN THE MIDST OF PLENTY,
by Ben H. Bagdikian. Copyright © 1964 by Ben H.
Bagdikian.
Harper & Row Publishers: From DARK GHETTO, by
Kenneth Clark.
Southern Regional Council, Inc.: From "The Migrant
Farmer," by Robert Coles.
Teachers College Press: From EDUCATION IN DE-
PRESSED AREAS edited by A. Harry Passow. Copy-
right © 1963 by Teachers College, Columbia University.
The Viking Press, Inc.: From EDUCATION AND IN-
COME, by Patricia Cayo Sexton. Copyright © 1961
by Patricia Cayo Sexton. All rights reserved.

Acknowledgments

A MAJOR PORTION of this book was written under the auspices of the New Jersey Department of Institutions and Agencies, Division of Mental Retardation, supported in part by a grant from the Social and Rehabilitation Service of the U.S. Department of Health, Education and Welfare. The guidance and support of Dr. Maurice Kott, director of the New Jersey Division of Mental Retardation, was essential to the successful completion of this work.

I would also like to express my sincere gratitude to Mr. Norman Loewenthal not only for the chapters which he wrote on Welfare, Health and the Migrants but also for his editorial assistance and his intense interest in this report. I am also grateful to Mr. Ronald Marlowe for his essay on Organic Impairment.

I give special thanks to my wife, Ann Hollinshead Hurley, both for her essay on Newark and for her thoughtfulness which has been so important to me.

R.L.H.

Contents

Foreword

by Edward M. Kennedy

There is a lot to be done in America if we are to reach a goal set for us almost two centuries ago—and a truly revolutionary goal it was, to dare insist upon "life, liberty, and the pursuit of happiness" for each and every one of our citizens. Clearly, not all of us, even today, however rich and mighty our nation is, have the kind of freedom, the kind of opportunities, to let a person fulfill the dreams a man like Thomas Jefferson had for all his countrymen.

Indeed, a book like this one by Rodger Hurley shows us how terrible *life* can be for some people among us; how little real *liberty* such people have; and how vain and frustrating and unsatisfying their *pursuit of happiness* must be. Yet at least this book has been written, and at least those who read it will find the usual rationalizations and self-deceptions we are all tempted to use a little more difficult in the face of the impressive evidence summoned by a man who has spent a good deal of time studying the problems of the poor, and in particular those among them we all too conveniently choose to call "mentally retarded."

There is indeed something self-serving about the way we often tend to think of the mentally retarded. The term has about it for many of us a final, unyielding quality; it is as if an irreversible hand of fate has been at work, and now the deed is done, the judgment pronounced, the person's mind declared "retarded"—and that is that. The rest, we say, is a custodial matter, or the rest is up to the particular families of the retarded, who will surely do the little that can be done, will surely help the retarded in the small and undramatic ways they can be helped.

No, says Mr. Hurley, such an attitude will not do, not if we take a careful look at the facts. His book does just that: it offers in clear and direct language a comprehensive survey of what biologists, sociologists, psychologists and physicians have managed to discover about (so it turns out) millions and millions of people who, to a very significant extent, are waiting. They are waiting for the rest of us to know what is already known; but more important, to do what can be and ought to be done. For the fact is that only a very small number of the children called "retarded" cannot profit substantially from various kinds of special attention. What is more, most children called "retarded" are not suffering from an injury or an inherited deficit, but from what might properly be called a kind of political, social and moral retardation afflicting the rest of us. In Mr. Hurley's words, "the supposed mental retardation of many of the poor is not mental retardation at all but environmental deprivation, which includes being 'served' by institutions that do not perform in the way the public believes they do. . . . It appears that on many occasions we are not measuring mental retardation but our society's callousness toward the poor."

If that seems a harsh and unsettling conclusion, there is unfortunately all too much corroboration for it in this book. The author cites one thoroughly convincing study whose essential (and striking) conclusion is that there is no known or irreversible cause for over 90 percent of the mental retardation in America—unless the cause be in fact a number of all too remediable social and economic forces that become translated, ultimately, into personal tragedies.

To me the real and important value of the book is in its candor. The author shows a willingness and ability to spell out what I have just mentioned, the manner in which abstractions like "poverty" and "prejudice" eventually get translated into the terribly sad psychological experiences of children who are called "backward" or "slow" or "dumb" or (by more sophisticated people) "retarded," when in fact they have gone hungry and become malnourished, and have been neglected and rebuffed and scorned and humiliated and made to feel unwanted and virtually subhuman.

No wonder, then, that hundreds of thousands of American children come to school and appear all too quiet, even dazed, or demonstrate confused and erratic behavior. Often they have from the very start lacked things: adequate medical care; the right food; a house that protects its inhabitants from cold weather and from mosquitoes and flies and rats; and in general, a neighborhood where children are safe, where their lives are held important, where their needs are met as a matter of course, and certainly as a matter of conscience. Of course such children become hurt and sad. Of course such children feel deep down inside a general doubt about the world, a mistrust of schools, of lessons that are assigned and explained, and of teachers who then test and grade them. It is natural that such children are labeled "retarded," and sent off here, there, anywhere—so long as they will be out of sight, out of our minds. Then we can always content ourselves with the knowledge that we have done the best we can, taken pains to look at them and test them and send them to those special classes which, as this book shows, all too often treat symptoms (and even these in a superficial way) rather than true causes.

Perhaps this book will help all those children—one can only hope and pray so. From now on, we will at least have a handy and straightforward summary of information which many Americans, I suspect, have all along sensed was available; information which, like most of the best scientific knowledge, confirms what sensitive and humane individuals have worried over and found cause for both sorrow and indignation. I hope particularly that the indignation many of us find growing within ourselves as we turn the pages of this book will turn into something else: a whole climate of opinion in this nation that enables us in the Congress to act, to pass the laws needed if American children of all races and creeds are no longer to be labeled and in essence ignored, but rather challenged finally to display their long hidden and neglected and overlooked possibilities, their humanity, really, which has been tragically squandered—to their loss and to our shame.

Poverty and Mental Retardation

ઠ I.

A New Assessment

Introduction

Among the conditions which have blighted American life, two of the most perplexing have been poverty and mental retardation. The harshness of each has been abetted by a good deal of public ignorance and, until recently, each has been treated with an astonishing degree of public apathy. A relationship between the two has rarely been made apparent; each has, in fact, been similarly relegated to regions beyond the American conscience.

The paradox of poverty-in-the-midst-of-plenty has been one of the most disturbing realizations of the American public in recent years. For many people this paradox has indicated the need for massive programs to correct the situation. For others, however, it has served to reinforce a number of deeply rooted attitudes, prejudices and myths concerning the indigent. Briefly stated, the belief of some people is that poverty can be attributed only to an inherent inferiority of the poor. This belief was frankly and brutally expressed by a New Jersey grower, who referred to the migrant workers on his farm as "nothing. . . . They never were nothing, they never will be nothing and you and me and God Almighty ain't going to change them." [1]

Mental retardation, too, has been the subject of even more persistent myths. Its existence has generally been blamed on an unfortunate heredity or simply labeled as an act of God. The suggestion that its roots lie closer to earth— that its most important causes are related to an unsatisfactory environment—has not penetrated the public mind. Perhaps the reason for this is that an unsuitable environment is associated with poverty, and it is popularly believed that poverty is a condition of inferior beings. The idea that a causal relationship links poverty and mental retardation, then, is simply at odds with the erroneous belief that poverty is the condition of people who are capable of achieving nothing better.

Popular attitudes toward retardation are characterized not only by adherence to long-standing prejudices but also by an appalling degree of ignorance. Of one hundred men and women interviewed in a Minnesota study, "only 1 in 10 demonstrated specialized information about retardation. One-fifth of the people interviewed confused retardation with other physical and mental disorders. The most common descriptions were related to mental ineffectiveness and the irresponsible nature of the retarded. Over half of S's [subjects] had neither heard nor read about mental retardation in the several months preceding the interview." [2] A second study revealed that these misconceptions prevail even among college students. [3]

This widespread prejudice and ignorance often cloud the clear fact that poverty in America is one of the most significant causes of mental retardation. It contributes to retardation far beyond the more publicized damage believed done by heredity or *uncontrollable* accidents suffered by prominent, prosperous families. Because of their poverty the poor endure the tragedy of mental retardation to a much greater degree than any other socio-economic class. "The majority of the mentally retarded are the children of the more disadvantaged classes of our society. This extraordinarily heavy prevalence in certain deprived groups suggests a major causative role, in some way not fully delineated, for adverse social, economic, and cultural factors. These conditions may not only mean absence of the physical necessities of life, but the lack of opportunity and motivation." [4]

Further, the *Connecticut Mental Retardation Planning Report* emphasized that the high prevalence of mental retardation among the poor is unrelated to the intellectual endowment of this class: "An important factor, repeatedly brought out by numerous studies, is that a disproportionate number of the retarded come from culturally deprived populations, and that a high percentage of this group is retarded in function rather than lacking in endowment. The environment from which they come does not provide the stimulation needed for healthy development and often breeds mental retardation as well as other serious health, psychological, and social problems." [5]

The main purpose of this paper is to delineate the relationship between poverty and mental retardation and to place mental retardation in its true perspective as a social pathology which thrives especially in the ghetto. Because of our society's failure to provide a suitable human environment for all its citizens, the children of the poor (who offer the same beauty and the same human potential as children from other socio-economic classes) have a much greater chance of becoming prostitutes, juvenile delinquents, criminals, unemployed—or mentally retarded. Too many children of the poor become, inevitably, waste products of a subhuman existence.

It should be noted that retardation is only one of a number of social pathologies that thrive in poverty. This relationship was identified accurately by the President's Panel on Mental Retardation when it concluded that "the conditions which spawn many other health and social problems are to a large extent the same ones which generate the problem of mental retardation. To be successful in preventing mental retardation on a large scale, a broad attack on the fundamental adverse conditions will be necessary." [6]

Within the folklore of every nation are rationalizations for the structure of that society. America is not an exception; here, as elsewhere, men rarely make decisions based on rational considerations. They are too often motivated by economic, social and psychological motives that they themselves often do not understand and could not explain. Accordingly, "upward mobility"—the Horatio Alger "rags-to-riches" myth—has never been possible for all Americans, despite what we have been led to believe. Equal opportunity has never been a reality in any society: "The weight of evidence seems to be that *nowhere* in a stratified society are equal opportunities open to all people. In school, as in the world at large, opportunities are usually open to students or closed to them in accordance with their social position. The higher the position, the more opportunities they have. Or, to put the formula another way: the more students *have,* the more they *get*—in school and in life." [7]

Disturbingly, this stratification is more rigid in the United States than elsewhere, for "painful as it may be to face, estimates are that the worker's child in the USSR has *twice* as good a chance of going to college as his US counterpart . . . an ugly fact, but one we must permit to crawl out from under its rock." [8]

Throughout our history, and to this day, entrepreneurs have used great political and economic power to maintain a docile, uneducated, unskilled labor force. Earlier in our history the rationalization for the economically lucrative or socially desirable slave system was found in the foreign culture of the African Negro, who was excluded from American citizenship because he was not "human." And, of course, the Calvinist equation of social and economic success with goodness remains a part of our Puritan heritage. The joy of being successful is intensified by the belief that to be successful one must be good. Further psychic gratification comes from the belief that those of lower status deserve their lot because they are inferior.

These statements suggest that a new and better-reasoned orientation to socio-economic, cultural and ethnic differences is needed if these variations are to be understood rather than falsely regarded as bases for discrimination. With a new awareness of the nature of our society and of the deprivation inherent in poverty, a more valid and human appreciation of mental retardation will be possible. Indeed, the unspoken biases of our society which have resulted in separate treatment for "unequal" people will no longer be considered justifiable. For the significant premise still remains that "the average innate capacity of children in one socio-economic cultural group does not differ substantially from the capacity of children in another group. Therefore, the wide differences in IQ among children from the different groups must be due primarily to differences in cultural opportunity." [9]

This lack of cultural opportunity is only one feature of poverty which enables it to squander human potential. Another is that life in poverty means a life full of immediate physical barriers—from inadequate nutrition to poor prenatal care—which can impair intellectual performance. Poverty is not to be seen as merely a passive condition; it does not simply fail to provide the stimulation considered essential to healthy development, but *actively* imperils the physical well-being of the individual and makes it doubly unlikely that his mental development will be satisfactory. The lack of cultural opportunity and the immediate physical danger establish a close link between poverty and retardation. Neither element alone is sufficient to explain the relationship fully, but together they extend the previously recognized dimensions of the problem.

The Traditional Orientation to Heredity, Poverty and Retardation

The thinking of experts concerning poverty and mental retardation is even more tragic than the ignorance of the general public. Unfortunately, many such experts harbor prejudiced opinions as to the importance of heredity in causing mental retardation, and in turn they equate poverty with genetic inferiority. Although one can understand the difficulty of the professional in bridging the gulf between his middle-class orientation and that of the poor, it might be expected that professional training would enable him to overcome his ignorance and prejudice.

The misconceptions date back at least to 1912, when Henry H. Goddard published *The Kallikak Family, A Study in the Heredity of Feeblemindedness*.[10] In this study, the genealogical history of the Kallikak family was examined through several generations; a high percentage of the members were identified as feebleminded, criminal, or poor. Goddard concluded that the Kallikaks were genetically inferior and that they passed this inferiority from father to son. Both conclusions were accepted enthusiastically as "scientific" law. The pernicious and widespread influence of *The Kallikak Family*, and similar, subsequent works is operative today in the personal attitudes of many mental retardation specialists, despite three crucial facts: Goddard's research model has been discredited; many researchers since Goddard have irrefutably demonstrated the importance of environment for intellectual development; and even the concept of the inheritability of mental abilities has yet to be proven.

In contrast to the biased thinking of many mental retardation workers, Seymour Sarason and Thomas Gladwin have introduced a more justifiable approach to the question of genetics. They are acutely aware of the major recent findings of many of their colleagues, especially

> . . . that an hereditary determinant of mental capacity must not be assumed to exist until proven. Furthermore, proof should be sought in terms of our present knowledge of human genetics and of the nature of human intellect, rather than, as is commonly done, through the administration of routine intelligence tests to a variety of "racial" and other groups. We do not propose to deny that heredity is a factor, particularly in mental deficiency (organic dysfunction), but rather that we should leave it out of accounting until it is supported by more than speculation and bias. Although scientifically we must retain an open mind, we must also recognize that among laymen and among many physicians and other professionals the assumption of a genetic determinant is customarily accepted. A considerable educational effort will therefore be necessary before they can even share our state of open-mindedness. The belief is widespread that even moderate subnormality results from a defect in heredity and is therefore irreversible.[11]

Research estimates of the percentage of cases of mental retardation caused by heredity have, over a period of many years, gradually decreased. Unfortunately, this trend has dissipated only in a minor degree those rigid, professional attitudes that have been nurtured for over a half a century.

Some of the more recent estimates of the percentage of cases of mental retardation caused by heredity are still as high as 50 percent.[12]

Hollingworth, 1920 . . . . 90%
Wallin, 1922 . . . . 62.9%
Tredgold, 1929 . . . . 80%
Rosanoff, et al. 1937 . . . . 50%
Yannet, 1945 . . . . 44.6% [13]

R. C. Schreerenberger (1965) estimates that 15 percent of all cases of MR (Mental Retardation) are due to genetic causes.[14] Any figure is at best an experienced guess. However, in view of Sarason and Gladwin's conclusion that retardation should be ascribed to genetics only where it can be scientifically substantiated, it is probable that future research will prove that even the 15 percent estimate is too high.

Closely related to the distorted emphasis on heredity as the preponderant cause of mental retardation are professional attitudes toward poverty, for one prejudice compounds the other. This is particularly evident in medicine and in medical institutions: "Organized medicine has spoken almost with a single voice, that of the American Medical Association, for decades. . . . The week before last the American Medical Association at its annual convention in Atlantic City, inaugurated a new president, Dr. Milford O. Rouse, of Dallas. In his inaugural address and another speech later in the week, he issued a strong challenge to the 'concept of health care as a right, rather than a privilege.' He called for renewed and revitalized opposition by doctors to government participation in health care planning." [15]

Dr. Rouse's speeches, the position of the American Medical Association on this and other issues, and the personal attitude of many medical professionals indicate that they believe the poor to be shiftless people who are causing unnecessary disturbances. Medical people seem wedded to the idea that "if only they were not so lazy, they would enjoy the American standard of living as we do." That equal opportunity to educate oneself or to obtain a high-income job does not exist fails to dissuade them from this attitude.

Dr. Rouse's position is a classic example of the type of thinking that has perpetuated a poverty cycle over generations. Without adequate medical care it is almost impossible for an individual to compete successfully in a complex and demanding society; but without the financial rewards of success, medical care simply cannot be obtained. It is particularly difficult to understand how the "privilege" of health care can be earned by a child; it is easier to appreciate that by the time money can be scraped together for some kind of medical attention, the child may no longer need it. It may be too late.

Educators, too, have been responsible for the perpetuation of the poverty cycle. The comprehensive evaluation that is now being made of education in America has found the system gravely deficient. Many auditors decry the crustaceanlike "middle classness" of the educational establishment; they trace the academic failure of poor children largely to the prejudices of their teachers.[16] Lee Rainwater emphatically supports this contention and broadens this attack to include the whole slum school system: "Slum schools now function more to stultify and discourage slum children than to stimulate and train them. The capacity of educators to alibi their lack of commitment to their charges is protean." [17] And the educational institution, more than any other, determines who is and who is not mentally retarded. In New Jersey, based on IQ statistics alone, a significant number of schools, especially in the heavily urbanized areas, contain up to a 50 percent ratio of children who could be considered mentally retarded—and these are not Special Education schools.[18]

The value of mental retardation literature and the quality of community discussion of this subject is further reduced because only two academic disciplines, medicine and education, have dominated the field; social science professionals have shown little or no interest. Unchallenged by researchers from other fields, mental retardation experts have responded to social and institutional, rather than to human, needs. Each specialist has viewed mental retardation in the light of the service his institution provides; neither has taken the responsibility for understanding the environment of the poor or for examining the socio-political process in order to improve that environment.

One result of this perspective is that the medical profession has isolated the etiology of mental retardation as its exclusive province. This extremely unfortunate situation—which is supported by public ignorance of mental retardation—is stated succinctly by George Tarjan (past president of the American Association on Mental Deficiency and vice-chairman of the President's Panel on Mental Retardation): "The main responsibility for primary and secondary prevention rests with the medical profession." [19] The effect of this medical domination of the field has been to insure that the bulk of past research on mental retardation is unrelated to the *needs* of the great majority of the mentally retarded. Regrettably, public resources continue to be channeled into purely medical research rather than into more promising areas.[20]

Not only has MR been dominated by two disciplines, but the number of workers in these fields has been small. Hopefully, appeals for help will be made more often and will be heeded. In their report, Sarason and Gladwin make such an appeal: "One of our primary objectives in writing this report is to present the problem in terms which we hope will encourage social scientists, who have thus far been almost totally uninterested, to view mental subnormality as an important research area. We also hope to lure more psychologists, psychiatrists, and others whose disciplines are already somewhat represented in the field, to join our ranks, and perhaps provide them with a few free perspectives." [21]

A recent (1959) paper indicates the tremendous amount of work that remains to be done in retardation research. After concluding that minority groups were over-represented in a particular state hospital for the retarded, the authors stated: "While traditionally mental retardation has been the province of medicine, psychology and education, the findings of this study suggest that there should be increasing recognition of the contributions of sociological analysis." [22]

It is lamentable that this recognition has come so recently and has been so little publicized, for mental retardation is a socio-political problem intimately related to public attitudes, to the allocation of public resources, and to institutional performance. The thesis around which this paper is built—that there is a strong causal link between poverty and mental retardation—demands that the whole question of mental retardation be approached from an entirely new and much wider point of view. The traditional narrowness of researchers in this field must not be permitted to interfere with a proper understanding of this staggering social problem.

The Meaning of Mental Retardation

One of the first priorities in developing a new approach to the problem of retardation is the need to adopt a suitable definition for the term "mental retardation." The phrase has been used rather freely in the preceding pages, and it is necessary at this point to identify more concretely the phenomenon to which it refers. Unfortunately, it is not possible to rely on any one of many definitions presently in use. As one expert has written: "The first major problem we encounter is the lack of an adequate and universally accepted definition of mental deficiency. We use a variety of names, such as mental deficiency, mental retardation, or mental subnormality. Some consider these terms synonymous; others attach a different meaning to each. When asked for a precise definition we cannot overcome even the first hurdle." [23] The accuracy of this statement is demonstrated by the situation in New Jersey, where the standards used to place children in Special Education are "as varied and as numerous as the approximately four hundred school psychologists in the State." [24]

Certainly one reason for the elusiveness of an adequate definition is that mental retardation has numerous causes, many of which are not precisely understood. A more basic reason is the tendency of the researcher to define retardation exclusively in terms of his own discipline. This practice helps to explain why a person who is considered retarded at an early stage of his life may later be considered "normal." The needs of the individual become clearly subordinate to those of the profession or the institution.

From an educational point of view, for example, retardation may have the meaning given to it by Christine P. Ingram: "The terms 'mentally retarded' or 'mentally handicapped' are applied to those who measure approximately 50 to 75 IQ, the lowest 2 percent of the school population in learning ability." [25] It will be shown later that currently used IQ tests are almost completely inadequate for evaluating the intellectual potential of the poor. And the IQ test is merely a part of one of several narrow approaches to the problem of retardation.

An entirely different approach is that of George A. Jervis, who views mental deficiency from the medical point of view "as a condition of arrested or incomplete mental development induced by disease or injury before adolescence or arising from genetic causes." [26]

A more precise definition is offered by Edgar A. Doll, who deals with the individual obviously in need of institutional care: "The mentally deficient person is (1) socially incompetent—that is, socially inadequate and occupationally incompetent and unable to manage his own affairs; (2) mentally subnormal; (3) retarded intellectually from birth or early age; (4) retarded at maturity; (5) mentally deficient of constitutional origin, through heredity or disease, and (6) essentially incurable." [27]

These definitions reflect various limited outlooks, and this parochial approach has operated against a unified understanding of the problem. A standard tailored to the demands of a particular profession may have the virtue of apparent objectivity, but the application of this standard is so narrow as to be useless for evaluating the large majority of the mentally retarded. A strictly medical definition lacks relevance for the individual who has no organic deficiency but whose intellectual performance is nevertheless extremely poor.

Difficulty does not end here: researchers, as has been noted, are victims not only of their own parochial professional viewpoints but also of popular prejudices. These prejudices creep into the application of even the most narrow of definitions. The rigid use of IQ scores, for example, inevitably works to the disadvantage of poor people by judging them according to standards which are valid, at best, only for the middle class.

But the greatest damage done by prejudice is its effect on another group of definitions which erroneously appear broad enough on the surface to include all aspects of mental retardation. The subjectivity with which these definitions are necessarily applied leaves them open to the whole range of common prejudices. As a result, such definitions fail to emphasize the environmental basis of mental retardation. Even the definition of Seymour Sarason, undeniably a pioneer in a broader understanding of mental retardation, leaves vague the role of environmental factors in producing inferior intellectual performance. He asserts that the mentally retarded are "individuals who, for temporary or chronic reasons, function intellectually below the average of their peer groups, but whose social adequacy is not in question or, if it is in question, there is the likelihood that the individual can learn to function independently and adequately in the community." [28]

An additional danger results from the middle-class bias of mental retardation specialists. Just as this bias leads them to ignore the environmental *causes* of retardation, it also leads them to evaluate intellectual ability according to middle-class *standards*. This second aspect of the environmental problem weakens the preeminent American Association on Mental Deficiency definition of retardation: "Mental retardation refers to subaverage general intellectual functioning which originates during the developmental period and is associated with impairment in adaptive behavior." [29] The meaning of "adaptive behavior" is wide open for interpretation. The practice has generally been to evaluate individuals by their ability to adapt not to the standards of their own socio-economic group, but to those of the middle class.

The problem, then, is not so much one of definition as one of understanding the biological, social and economic damage done to poor children in America—and of attempting to eliminate the conditions which can produce retardation. Poor people not only suffer more often from mental deficiency but also are apt to be measured unfairly because of their station in life. A universally applicable standard would be possible only in a utopian state where equal opportunity and social justice were realities. The researcher should not despair of progress in a nonutopian world. Rather, he should approach the problem from an entirely new standpoint—that of the predominance of socio-economic factors.

This approach, moreover, will make possible a clarification in definition that has remained hidden. The term "mental retardation" should be used to designate only those who suffer from hereditary, organic, or injury-based defects which impair intellectual functioning. It should be noted, of course, that many in this category are the victims of poverty. Although bad genes and other *uncontrollable* accidents strike with equal force at all levels of society, it is the poor who are at the mercy of a myriad of other misfortunes, from bad nutrition to lead-paint poisoning, which can permanently damage the brain.

An even larger group—those among the poor whose cultural and psychological backgrounds simply prevent them from performing adequately in middle-class society—are best referred to as "environmentally deprived." This term should replace the designation of "culturally-familially retarded" that is used to describe about 80 percent of those now considered mentally retarded. In a more just and enlightened society, these people would demonstrate the same range of intellectual ability as that shown by the middle class.

One final note is necessary: while the distinction between "mental retardation" and "environmental deprivation" is useful in understanding the problem, the two phenomena may not be as easy to separate in practice. It may be almost impossible, for example, to tell the difference between that child who is mentally retarded due to poor nutrition during the prenatal period and the one whose cultural deprivation causes him to appear retarded when viewed by the middle-class observer. The significant point is that *both* are the children of poverty and both are symbols for the need to examine, with a new attitude, the conditions of life among the poor.

The Meaning of Poverty

Because poverty is conventionally defined as a lack of adequate financial resources, one may use a figure of income to differentiate between those families who are poor and those who are not. The figure selected by the United States Office of Economic Opportunity is three thousand dollars per year for a family of four.[30] It appears, however, that this figure—arbitrary at best and now several years old —severely underestimates the financial needs of the American family. In fact, the Federal Bureau of Labor Statistics estimates that for a worker's family with two children in New York $5,970 is needed to maintain a "modest but adequate" standard of living. If a recent Teamsters Union study is based on this figure, then 49 percent of New York City families are classified as deprived. Furthermore, 70.8 percent of New York Negro and Puerto Rican families would be classified as deprived according to this study.[31]

For residents of New Jersey, living in the shadow of New York City, the dimensions of the problem are similar. Even using the conservative three-thousand-dollar figure, the New Jersey Office of Economic Opportunity calculates that one million poor people live in the state today.[32] Since New Jersey ranks eighth in the nation in average per-capita income,[33] it is evident that the state is characterized by an unusually wide discrepancy betwen rich and poor.

Poverty is much more than a lack of money. A "culture of poverty" is born in the slums and grows with the child from the wrong family, the wrong region of the country, or the wrong ethnic or racial group. This "self-perpetuating" nature of poverty merits careful attention: "Basic to the economics of delinquency is the transmission of poverty across the generations. Today, for the 18-year-old, employment is hard to find. What chance has a slum-dwelling 6-year-old to break out of the cycle of poverty? Individual initiative may be important in determining an individual's destiny, but it is the economic and social forces shaping the way children are brought up, their preparation for adulthood by public institutions, their chances for self-improvement that perpetuate poverty." [34]

This culture of poverty becomes a legacy of psychological distortion, and manifests itself in a profound alienation from the larger society and from other people, an intense feeling of powerlessness, and a belief in the meaninglessness of struggle. The degradation and spiritual depression of poverty are omnipresent; they affect every action that makes up the poor man's "life style." The very contrast between the material life of the poor and that of the affluent society produces an invidious comparison which is psychologically damaging to those who are poverty stricken. Because our national values stress success and high achievement, we applaud efforts at self-improvement and advancement. The world of advertisement stimulates desires for status and material rewards—and shows the splendid benefits afforded those who achieve. This evident wealth, plus the knowledge that some people have actually begun at the bottom and reached the top, makes the poor feel guilty for their lack of achievement and even more self-conscious of their deprivation. It is the relativity of their deprivation— the constant contrast they see—that perhaps more than anything else, says Lola Irelan, affects their own life view, and leads them to believe themselves failures.[35]

The general attitude of our society, as expressed either

consciously or unconsciously, is a weapon which brutalizes and defeats the poor. As long as the poor are considered to be spiritually corrupt, this will be so. Ben H. Bagdikian, author of *In the Midst of Plenty*, supports this point with a personal illustration:

> One hour before, I had left a room in the Palmer House. On the way to a shower stall at Union Station, while I still had on a conventional business suit, I stopped at a busy orange drink stand and asked the young girl to change a dollar bill. She did and handed me the change with a pleasant, "yes sir." Twenty minutes later I came back in paint-splotched shoes, old black trousers, khaki shirt, and ragged sweater, a wrinkled threadbare raincoat, the part out of my hair, carrying an old brown canvas zipper bag. I asked the girl for an orange drink and she served me, holding the drink until I had put the money on the counter, her face frozen and hostile and never looking directly at me. I already felt the blank wall between me and respectable society by which a man can walk as though invisible. If he asks directions he may get no answer, as though his voice made no sound, or he may get a flash of fear and revulsion in the eye of the man he asks. It is remarkably easy to become an emotional exile from one's own society.[36]

Personality is disrupted when one is poor in America; self-image is besmirched. Hope and the drive to succeed are usually inexorably rooted out of the human psyche. Finally, by the time slum children reach their sixth or seventh year they have fully absorbed the values of the slum and are psychologically unfit for taking advantage of opportunities or changes which may offer themselves as they develop in their lifetime.[37] Beyond this, the human disaster of poverty is overlaid with the image of the "well-intentioned" citizen, aghast at the inability of the poor to take advantage of minimal opportunities, even though these opportunities are "offered" in a condescending, patronizing manner, and many years too late.

On a national basis, in this land of unparalleled wealth, government officials acknowledge that approximately thirty-five million people are poor, even though the average national family income exceeds seven thousand dollars per year. Of white families 14.4 percent are under the poverty line. At the same time 36 percent of the nonwhite families, 90 percent of whom are Negroes, are suffering from poverty.[38] The nonwhite population in America is deprived in far greater proportions than the larger white population, although the actual number of poor whites is substantially larger.

The heritage of slavery, racism—a reiterated, visible, virulent aspect of American life—along with the concomitant economic deprivation, have produced misery for the American Negro on such a scale and in such depth that it is impossible for a white man to comprehend it fully. The pathological impact on a human being of race prejudice alone, ignoring the added evil of poverty, is impossible to overestimate. An American Negro, James Weldon Johnson, declared: "This [segregation and discrimination] is the dwarfing, warping, distorting influence which operates upon each and every coloured man in the United States. He is forced to take his outlook on all things, not from the viewpoint of a citizen, or a man, or even a human being, but from the view-point of a *coloured* man." [39] J. H. Griffin, who artificially colored his skin black, notes well in *Black Like Me* the "hate stare" which has been a common Negro experience. "It came from a middle-aged, heavy-set, well-dressed white man. He sat a few yards away, fixing his eyes on me. Nothing can describe the withering horror of this. You feel lost, sick at heart before such unmasked hatred." [40]

The impact of racism on the life of the American Negro, especially the poor Negro, cannot be minimized. The utter degradation of Negro experience is central to the problem of poverty and mental retardation. But if the poor Negro has suffered from the stigma of race, the poor white has suffered from the stigma of not having succeeded in a society which places few racial barriers before him. A white man's failure in an America which preaches "upward mobility" is of itself a unique indictment of inferiority. To what else can a white man's poverty be ascribed? The effect of being considered "white trash" at least approximates that of being branded "nigger"; the poor white man, like the poor black man, has his own special burden to bear. John Steinbeck, in *The Grapes of Wrath,* delineated the meaning of this burden:

> "You never been called 'Okie' yet."
>
> Tom said, "Okie. What's that?"
>
> "Well, Okie use' ta mean you was from Oklahoma. Now it means you're a dirty son-of-a-bitch. Okie means you're scum. Don't mean nothing itself, it's the way they say it." [41]

It would be a mistake to attribute to racism effects which properly belong to poverty. As Oscar Lewis suggests,

> The concept of the culture of poverty may help to correct misapprehensions that have ascribed some behavior patterns of ethnic, national, or regional groups as distinctive characteristics. For example, a high incidence of common-law marriage and of households headed by women has been thought to be distinctive of Negro family life in this country and has been attributed to the Negro's historical experience of slavery. In actuality it turns out that such households express essential traits of the culture of poverty and are found among diverse peoples in many parts of the world and among peoples that have had no history of slavery . . . its practitioners (of the culture of poverty) exhibit remarkable similarity in the structure of their families, in interpersonal

relations, in spending habits, in their value systems and in their orientation in time.[42]

Thus, studies of poverty for the two racial groups will be used interchangeably, and although many deal with the poor Negro, their validity is not limited to that group. A life in poverty is similar in many ways for both white and black and its end result is exactly the same—exclusion from an environment in which proper human development can take place.

The Basis for Evaluating Intelligence

It is impossible to discuss the current methods of assessing mental retardation without considering the traditional and fallacious understanding of intelligence as a fixed, unchangeable entity which supposedly unfolds according to a natural, predetermined process. This traditional concept of intelligence has had widespread influence despite the admonitions of Alfred Binet, who created the IQ test and who studied intelligence for over twenty years:

> . . . some recent philosophers appear to have given their moral support to the deplorable verdict that the intelligence of an individual is a fixed quantity. . . . We must protest and act against this brutal pessimism. . . . A child's mind is like a field for which an expert farmer has advised a change in the method of cultivating, with the result that in place of desert land, we now have a harvest. It is in this particular sense, the one which is significant, that we say that the intelligence of children may be increased. One increases that which constitutes the intelligence of a school child, namely, the capacity to learn, to improve with instruction.[43]

The belief in a fixed quantum of intelligence is intimately related to the previously mentioned attitudes of past researchers concerning the significance of heredity in the etiology of MR. If one concludes that mental subnormality is solely a genetic failure and that social and intellectual performance are unrelated to environment, it follows that mental potential is static and unchangeable. This notion was so dominant in the 1920's that marked fluctuation of one's IQ was usually attributed to invalid testing procedures. In response to this misinterpretation, Stoddard has commented that "to regard all changes in mental status as an artifact is to shut one's eyes to the most significant and dramatic phenomenon in human growth." [44]

Early investigators believed that, barring any disastrous environmental interferences, intelligence would manifest itself in a predictable manner. Thomas Pettigrew states that this belief was supported by studies of salamanders and Hopi Indian children in which the authors concluded that as physical and genetic structures grew, intelligence also grew and that thus prior experience was not needed for intellectual growth.[45] C. Burt was a proponent of the position that intelligence "is inherited or at least innate, not due to *teaching* or *training.*" [46]

Modern social scientists have discovered, however, that the "measured" intellectual difference which exists between poor and middle-class children is a function of a *lack* of a stimulating environment. The poor child does not reach the middle-class standard of achievement because he is immersed in a stultifying and culturally barren world. Numerous children have shown impressive IQ gains merely on the basis of being moved from a depressing environment to one which is less so. One of the most dramatic studies demonstrates that a change in financial resources alone may make possible a drastic change in academic performance. It was found that the children of Osage Indians, whose general performance on IQ tests was considerably below that of Negroes, met the national norms on these tests after the tribe became relatively prosperous due to the discovery of oil on their reservation.[47]

More significant are the changes in the style of life made possible by financial success. Human interaction in a stimulating environment replete with conversation and personal attention is at the crux of human growth. W. S. Neff states that "translation from a poor to a good environment brings about a large increase in IQ which, at the extremes, may amount to 30 or 40 points. . . . There is a strong possibility that the positive relation between age and social status does not exist below a certain age level. . . . Some evidence from identical twin studies indicates that there is a correlation of about $+.50$ between social status and intelligence even when heredity is held constant." [48]

O. Klineberg's research supports Neff's contention. Klineberg found that Negroes migrating from the rural South to New York City increased their IQ's significantly, an apparent reflection of the impoverished environment of the rural South when compared to the urban North. This improvement in environment produced an improvement on the Stanford-Binet test of 7.5 points—from eighty-one to 88.5—over a period of three to four years.[49] It is an outstanding rise, for the contrast between rural poverty and urban slum life is a relatively minor one.

The classic longitudinal study of the overriding importance of environment in intellectual growth, however, was done by Harold Skeels and Marie Dye (1939), and Skeels and Marie Skodak (1965). Twenty-five children from a children's shelter were chosen as a research group; thirteen who were considered to be retarded though not organically damaged were selected as an experimental group and twelve children who tested as normally intelligent were made the contrast group. The IQ for the experimental group ranged from thirty-five to seventy-seven with a mean of sixty-four and a median of sixty-five. This group was placed in wards with *mentally retarded* adult women who took great personal interest in the children and watched after them as if they were their own. Because of the wide age difference between the children, whose mean age was eighteen months, and these female retardates, the women played a role very similar to that of a mother of normal intellectual powers. The results speak eloquently for themselves.

The [experimental] children remained at the institution for the mentally retarded for periods which ranged from 5½ to 52 months. All gained in IQ by the end of their stay there from 7 to 45 points with a mean gain of 28 points. The individual IQ's now ranged from 79 to 113 with a mean of 92 and a median of 93. The youngest child was 7 months with an IQ of 89 when he was transferred to the institution from the orphanage, and returned in 5½ months with an IQ of 113. The oldest was 30 months with an IQ of 36 when he was transferred, and was 89 months with an IQ of 81 when he was returned to the orphange. On return, the lowest IQ was 79, representing a gain of 7 points in a child who was two years old when transferred and who remained in the institution nearly two years.

During this same period of time, the children in the contrast group were living the routine existence in the orphanage. The 12 children who met the criteria for the contrast group had their first examination between the ages of 12 and 22 months. At that time their IQ's ranged from 71 to 103 with a mean of 87 and a median of 90. These children were routinely given psychological tests, and three subsequent measures are available up to the age of 4½ years, or roughly the ages of the experimental group when they returned to the orphanage. The contrast group showed a steady decline in IQ so that by the mean age of 48 months the mean IQ was 51 and median was 60. With the exception of one child who had gained 2 points in IQ (from 81 to 83), all others lost 8 to 45 points. The mean loss in IQ was 26 points.

Essentially, then, the two groups had reversed positions. Those who had been retarded with a mean IQ of 64 were now normal, with a mean IQ of 92, while those who had been normal with a mean IQ 87 were now retarded, with a mean IQ 61.[50]

Even more dramatic are the findings of a survey on the same twenty-five children after an interval of twenty-one years:

> The median subject in the experimental group has completed the twelfth grade, while the median subject in the contrast group has completed only the third grade. One-third of the experimental subjects have been to college, and one has a baccalaureate degree. The whole range of occupations is represented in the experimental group, while in the contrast group "50 percent of the subjects are unemployed, and those that are employed are, with the exception of one person, unskilled laborers." [51]

Most spectacular of all is the case of one of the girls in the experimental group who had an original IQ of thirty-five: "This subject has graduated from high school, has one semester of college, is married, and has two children of IQ's of 128 and 107." [52]

Other studies show similar results: Kirk (1958) demonstrated that formalized pre-school training is of tremendous benefit both for children in the community and for children in institutions for the mentally retarded. While the lack of such training merely slowed the development of the community children, it meant a significant *drop* in the IQ level of the institutional children once they reached school age.[53] Pre-school training "may be especially important for 'culturally deprived' [institutional] children since . . . children from adequate homes who do not have pre-school experience show accelerated mental and social development after entering school, but children from inadequate homes do not show such acceleration, i.e., even after entering school 'deprived' children retain their lower level of mental and social performance." [54]

Dennis (1960) has stressed another important form of environmental deprivation and its effect on IQ level. Removing one- to two-year-old infants from an orphanage in Teheran—where they had received almost no attention—and placing them in an institution where they were "subjected to minimal manipulation and environmental change," Dennis found IQ increases of up to fifty points within a few months.[55] Richard Kobler and Robert E. Weber, reviewing these findings, have felt that they constitute a case of "cultural mutation." [56]

In a comprehensive study of the *Effects of Changing the Rearing Environment,* H. Carl Haywood evaluated these studies and their implications in these words: "One can hardly avoid the forcefulness of these demonstrations of the impact of environmental factors on the development of intelligence, either in their implications for what it is possible to do in a positive sense for those who are born or early placed in socially depressing environments, or in their indictment of our shamefully slow social progress toward actually doing what is possible to end tragic wastes of human resources." [57] "Fixity" of intelligence and predetermined development are concepts which have been repudiated scientifically but whose influence lingers on.

The Intelligence Quotient

The American Association on Mental Deficiency, the most highly respected organization in its field, and many state public school systems including New Jersey's system use IQ and Adaptive Behavior (both of which can be derived from written tests) as the basis for determining mental subnormality. But despite the rigid dependence of institutions on these criteria, this approach does not in any way measure the intellectual potential of the poor child. It serves only to reflect and reinforce middle-class prejudice.

Perhaps no single concept in any discipline has been as lethally criticized, by as many investigators, as that of IQ. Yet it remains a sanctified, unchallengeable point of reference for educators and for the middle class. Its potency is so great that it can generate an identity crisis in a child who is doing excellent school work but who discovers that his IQ is only average. Despite protestations to the contrary, it is used by teachers from the very first year of school as an untainted criterion that can be used to evaluate and categorize students. As an "accurate" measure of intellectual potential, it becomes the greatest influence in determining which child is to enter the enriched educational program and which is to be placed on the slower, inferior track.

The ingrained reliance of the educational establishment on IQ tests and the actual value of such tests are in direct contradiction. Several studies have attacked the concept. Allison Davis and Kenneth Eells indicate that the reasoning used in constructing the test is faulty. They maintain that test makers have used two criteria to prove that the test is valid for examining intelligence: the correlation between test scores and school grades and between chronological age and score. But they point out that many scholars, including Binet, have shown that school grades are not related to intelligence so much as to work habits, attentiveness, home environment, desire to compete, etc. And simply because a larger percentage of students can solve a given problem relative to their increasing age, this can not be accepted as valid proof of intelligence. It might only indicate more practice and instruction.[58]

As these authors suggest, the quality of the school and teacher are extremely important in scholastic performance. Much research indicates that the poor child receives inferior teaching and that he receives it in antiquated schools with substandard facilities.

The concept of an intelligence test is meaningful only if there exists some measurable quantity which represents intelligence. No such quantity has yet been discovered. "The fact is that there is no satisfactory objective criterion of true mental capacity, and therefore no possibility, at least at present, of constructing a satisfactory test of intelligence by purely objective means." [59] In view of the complexity of the human mind and human behavior it is not surprising that psychologists have been unable to define intelligence.

A most useful discussion of the failure of the IQ test is found in Sarason and Gladwin's book *Mental Subnormality*. They believe that intelligence is far more complex than has thus far been thought by experts. Intellectual function and capacity cannot be divorced from psychological processes and cultural settings. The assumptions made about causes of intellectual failure or retardation are based on four premises, two of which are false, two questionable. They conclude, therefore, that "recent studies on the nature and varieties of intellectual capacities strongly suggest that much of our present conceptions, and more of our practices, will have to be scrapped if our understanding is to be extended." [60]

A basic criticism of intelligence tests, to which they allude, is that they fail to include the range of intellectual abilities that are known to exist. To date, intelligence tests have evaluated only one aspect of intelligence. As pointed out in an article in the *New Republic,* the test measures accuracy, speed, ability to solve puzzles, to analyze rather than synthesize. The article concludes: "Taken together these limitations mean that a man can be socially imperceptive, personally insensitive and morally obtuse as well as scatterbrained, short sighted, and unimaginative all while being classified as supremely intelligent on the IQ meter." [61]

The arguments that have been presented thus far condemn the tests only as indicators of inherent potential. Little consideration has been given to the question of the socioeconomic class under examination. It is obvious that IQ tests are not able to measure the potential of even the middle class; a number of issues must be raised, then, as to the special irrelevancy of these tests for the poor.

Intelligence tests are invariably slanted toward the knowledge which the middle class has and the poor do not have. They are culturally biased. This point has been recognized by many investigators, and a few examples will suffice to support it. The vocabulary that is used in the early grades ·is the language of the middle class. The poor child has had no contact with that language in his home, either in written or the spoken form, and the very words used in school are foreign to the poor. Some examples of these words are "violin," "fireplace," "ocean liner," "chandelier," "dwarf" and "cash register."

Further, these tests often allude to experiences indigenous only to the middle-class child. In the early years of school, tests require the child to name the relationship between one animal and another. A child who has been to the zoo and has been told the names of the animals is, of course, more likely to answer correctly. One test requires completion of this problem: "Cub is to bear as gosling is to: 1. fox 2. grouse 3. goose 4. rabbit 5. duck." [62] It is most unlikely that a child from the Central Ward in Newark would know the differences among these animals without a zoo or picture-book experience. Moreover, as A. Anastasi and F. A. Cordova comment, it does not appear possible to avoid these difficulties by constructing a culturally unbiased test. "No test can be completely 'culture free,' or even 'culture constant,' since the content of any test will tend to favor one or another culture. The elimination of specific culturally limited information from a test is only a partial and superficial solution. Each culture stimulates the development of certain abilities and interests, and inhibits others. The resulting psychological differences will inevitably be reflected in test performance, as in other behavior of individuals reared in diverse cultural settings." [63]

The discussion so far has centered on the nature of intelligence tests, their limitations, and their bias in favor of the middle class. Left unmentioned are factors treated by Frank Riessman in his excellent chapter on intelligence tests in *The Culturally Deprived Child*.[64] To summarize that chapter, the poor child, especially the poor child who comes from a minority group, is fearful of many of the individuals whom he meets in the middle-class school. He does not identify with his teachers, nor do they identify with him. The result is that the child sees no necessity to perform and to compete with others. For the poor child, the classroom, and the school in general, is a place where one must constantly be wary of foreign persons. Yet it is in this atmosphere of fear and anxiety that the poor child is subjected to intelligence testing. Often the teacher, the central object of the child's distrust, administers the test. Quite obviously, these conditions do not make for satisfactory test performance by the poor child.

Practice for an IQ examination is also a factor which distinguishes the poor child from the children of other classes. Although poor children may have taken many IQ tests, it has been proven that many do not really understand how to take a test properly. Haggard gave a group of deprived children and nondeprived children three one-hour tests in which he explained, in language understandable to both groups, the thinking processes needed to solve the various problems. In addition, he offered rewards to the lower-class children for good performance. Under these conditions the IQ's of these children were improved markedly after only three hours of practice.[65]

A reward for the deprived children was necessary to stimulate them to compete. This was necessary, for as Martin Deutsch and others have demonstrated, the lack of competitive spirit in the poor child is a function of his home life. Competition and reward for good performance are practically nonexistent in impoverished, broken homes. Parents have neither the time nor the energy to set tasks for their children to perform, to observe their performance, and comment on their success. Nor do they have time to criticize poor performance or unfinished tasks. Unfortunately, much of the structure of classroom life is based on the assumption that a child will anticipate rewards for success and punishment for failure. The poor child is often baffled by this structure.[66] And, as Riessman states,

> In the area of motivation, it is clear that middle-class children are more motivated to do well on examinations of the IQ sort because of the general emphasis on success and competition in middle-class life. Even where an examination is not directly related to a reward or a threat, the middle class strives to perform well. Part of the differences in IQ scores of middle-class and deprived children is due to differences in strength of motivation to perform well on an examination rather than to differences in intelligence.[67]

One question remains unanswered. If the attack on IQ tests is so devastating, why does their influence remain so much in evidence? A few cities, such as New York, have officially downgraded the importance of IQ results. Unfortunately, no reform has been undertaken in the spirit of Davis's criticism: "Half of the ability in this country goes down the drain because of the failure of intelligence tests to measure the real mental ability of the children from the lower socio-economic groups and because of the failure of the schools to recognize and train this ability." [68]

The rationale for continued use of the IQ test is inextricably tied to middle-class prejudice. IQ is defended on the basis that it is a good device for predicting future academic achievement. That there are other, accurate indicators of future success, such as a qualified teacher's evaluation of the student, is largely unrecognized. As Sexton has emphasized, social class is also an accurate measure of school performance in our middle-class schools. Given a family's income, the educational background of both parents and location of the home, one can determine with considerable accuracy how the child will do in school. No educator, however, would dare to admit that socio-economic class may be used in this way—despite the fact that a poor child's academic failure is all too often his fate from birth.

The Concept of Adaptive Behavior

The second measure used to determine intellectual ability is an evaluation of adaptive behavior. In its recent monograph on terminology and classification of mental retardation, the American Association on Mental Deficiency states that adaptive behavior is associated during the school years with academic performance, and during adult life with vocational and social effectiveness, as well as with the degree of "strife and discord in family and community." [69]

The circularity involved in constructing this standard, especially for the poor child and the poor man, is obvious. If, as is most often the case, a culturally deprived child enters an inferior school, a school which is poorly equipped and not designed to deal with the special problems of such a child, he invariably fails to measure up to middle-class standards and often drops out of school; the failure in school follows the child to adulthood, for without an education one is relegated to menial jobs at substandard salaries. Crime, unemployment, broken homes and, most of all, profound personal unhappiness follow in sequence. The "strife and discord" in adulthood which seem to verify the prediction made about the child, are actually made inevitable by the deprivations of childhood.

The American Association on Mental Deficiency admits that no objective test measures adaptive behavior. No scientific standard can be used to determine which behavior is a function of inherent inferiority and which is a function of a cultural background that differs from that approved by the American Association on Mental Deficiency:

> Since adequate population norms and highly objective measures of the various aspects of adaptive behavior are not yet available, it is not possible to establish precise criteria of impaired functioning in these areas. At present, the most precise statement that may be made is that, for a judgment of inadequate or impaired social adjustment, learning or maturation, an individual's behavior in these areas must be clearly inefficient or subnormal as judged by the best standards available for the *comparison* of a person's performance level with that of the *general population.*[70]

The Association points out that because no test can gauge adaptive behavior, the analysis of this factor becomes a subjective estimate on the part of the examiner. "Though it is highly desirable that precise criteria of impairment be established for each supplementary term category, suitable measurement techniques, for the most part, have not yet been developed. Therefore, the determination of impairment in personal-social sensory-motor skill areas will be based to a great extent, on subjective clinical evaluation of the degree to which the person's behavior conforms to the standards and norms for the individual's age group." [71]

The more extended American Association on Mental Deficiency discussion of the different aspects of adaptive behavior makes clear its view that adaptive behavior is the classic behavior of the well-scrubbed, middle-class child. Direct reference below to the American Association on Mental Deficiency monograph captures the magnitude of this cultural bias:

Personal Social Factors

The individual with an impairment in interpersonal relations does not relate adequately to peers and/or authority figures and may demonstrate an inability to recognize the needs of other persons in interpersonal interactions. . . .

Impairment in Cultural Conformity

. . . behavior which does not conform to social mores, behavior which does not meet standards of dependability, reliability and trustworthiness; behavior which is persistently asocial, antisocial, and/or excessively hostile. . . .

Impairment in Responsiveness

Impaired or deficient responsiveness is characterized by an inability to delay gratification of needs and a lack of long range goal striving or persistence with response only to short-term goals.[72]

The failure of these standards to measure the mental capacity of the poor child is overwhelming. The categories and the exposition of them by the American Association on Mental Deficiency read as if they were taken from research specifically describing the life style of the poor. But it is this life style and the conditions producing it which the American Association on Mental Deficiency ignores in passing judgment on the slum child. "In the white and particularly in the Negro slum worlds little in the experience that individuals have as they grow up sustains a belief in a rewarding world. The strategies that seem appropriate are not those of a good, family-based life or of a career, but rather *strategies for survival.*" [73]

"Relates adequately to peers and/or authority figures," "dependable, reliable, trustworthy," "able to delay gratification of needs and develop and strive for long range goals"—

these are all qualities that the middle-class family can inculcate in the child. Time, money, security, prestige and external assistance available to the middle-class family insure the proper acculturation of the child. In the bowels of urban or rural poverty, however, no such resources exist; instead there is the alluring life of the other world of crime and dope that is symbiotic with poverty. "Their [the family's] influence is diluted and undermined by . . . the constant presence of temptation—drugs, drinking, gambling, petty thievery, prostitution." [74]

An incredible contrast exists between the demands of life for a child in the ghetto and a child from the suburbs. The imperative of survival must always remain at the core of a slum child's personality; the survival of a suburban child is rarely, if ever, in question. The commonplace dangers that a slum child faces, such as being mugged by an addict or beaten for lunch money by older boys, are epitomized by the replies of a nineteen-year-old boy:

"How do you feel about conditions here?"

"I don't know."

"What do you mean, you don't know. You're out here everyday."

"As long as I can survive, I don't care about nobody else, man."

"Is it rough out here in the streets trying to survive?"

"Yes, if you don't put your mind to it, you know, to do something to survive by, it's rough." [75]

The suggestion that the struggle for survival be abandoned in favor of a more "acceptable" way of life understandably meets with this kind of response: "Oh come on. Get off that crap. I make $40 to $50 a day selling marijuana. You want me to go down to the garment district and push one of these trucks through the street and at the end of the week take home $40 or $50 if I'm lucky? They don't have animals doing what you want me to do. There would be some society to protect animals if anybody had them pushing them damn trucks around. I'm better than an animal, but nobody protects me. Go away, mister. I got to look out for myself." [76]

Yet if the poor are unwilling to display the kind of adaptive behavior desired by the middle class, the major part of the responsibility belongs to the middle class. The characteristic response of society at large to the existence of poverty is to brand the poor as "asocial" and, at the same time, to take advantage of their desperate situation. In local newspapers almost every day some form of discrimination or aggrandizement at the expense of the poor is revealed. For example, the following appeared in *The New York Times:* "Deputy Mayor Timothy W. Costello said yesterday that a city survey indicated that residents of low-income neighborhoods may be paying as much as 15 percent more for food than those in middle-income areas." [77] Prices are higher for the poor; food stores in ghetto areas commonly raise prices during the few days following the mailing of welfare checks, as they do following the monthly issuance of food stamps. For racial minorities, of course, discrimination is even more acute. The equal employment opportunity law was passed three years ago but little progress has been made in the interim toward promoting or hiring Negroes at the higher levels of industry, banking, etc.[78]

Because of the unwillingness of the middle class to respond to this extremely serious situation, it is accurate to say that the "adaptive behavior" of this class—its ability to allocate its resources to pressing human needs—is rather unsatisfactory. In these terms, the apparently inferior adaptive behavior of the poor may be seen as a product of the spiritual impoverishment of the larger society; in no way does it reflect an inherent inferiority of the poor.

A quote in Michael Harrington's *The Other America*

poignantly demonstrates the desperate attempt made by some slum children to adapt to middle-class norms: "H. Warren Dunham studied forty catatonic schizophrenics in Chicago in the early forties. He found that none of them had belonged to gangs or had engaged in the kind of activity the middle class regards as abnormal. They had, as a matter of fact, tried to live up to the standards of the larger society, rather than conforming to the values of the slum. 'The catatonic young man can be described as a good boy and one who has all the desirable traits which all the social agencies would like to inculcate in the young man of the community.' " [79]

The Statistics of Mental Retardation

A long-standing assumption has been that a majority of the population is of normal intelligence. The force of this concept is so great that intelligence tests are developed and refined to insure that a graph of the results will produce a Gaussian, or bell-shaped, curve. In other words, the intelligence tests are manipulated through the use of various techniques to score results that test makers assume these tests should record. "In this tradition [of belief in the validity of the Gaussian curve] developers of intelligence tests have attempted to produce scales that give normal distributions when administered to the appropriate population. The idea that intelligence tests should give normal distributions is so firmly ingrained that psychological textbooks state that intelligence itself is distributed normally." [80]

As Clarke has suggested, the validity of this ingrained assumption remains to be proven. "The assumption can neither be proved nor disproved in detail since its criterion, the test, is arranged precisely to meet the requirements of normal distribution. Arguments about it are thus circular." [81]

Despite the relative success of test makers in securing a normal distribution of test scores, research indicates that the normal curve is skewed at the lower end. Pearson and Jaederhold, in a generally accepted study, emphasized this point as early as 1914.[82] P. U. Lemkau supported this conclusion in more recent times.[83] Apparently the normal curve is *not* normal.

Implications of this study are many. The fact that the bell-shaped curve is skewed to the left damages the validity of the original assumption that intelligence is normally distributed. Since the validity of intelligence evaluation scores is itself highly questionable, does it matter how these scores are distributed? Further, does it matter that a certain percentage of the population is theoretically *supposed* to be mentally retarded on the basis of an IQ test?

In view of the traditional myths concerning the poor, it is not difficult to see that the expectation of a certain amount of mental retardation in the population is neatly confirmed by the existence of a certain amount of poverty. Likewise, the existence of poverty can be justified on the basis of a predictable quantity of retardation—that is, inherent inferiority. The normal distribution of intelligence is a perfect explanation for a "normal" state of affairs in which a sizeable segment of the population is poor. But because of the dramatic importance of a stimulating, enriched environment, who can say that the people who are of high socioeconomic status and who are now largely represented on the upper half of the bell-shaped curve do not belong on the lower half? Since the poor are obviously disadvantaged vis-à-vis the larger society, can it be proven that with true equal opportunity the poor would not in general have a greater fund of intellectual ability than people who at present have received every advantage that life in America has to offer?

Using the conventional reasoning, the Presidential

Panel on Mental Retardation and nearly every other major organization in the field of mental retardation contends that about 3 percent of the population, approximately six million people, is mentally retarded.[84] This figure is widely used despite the fact that it has never been proven. "No comprehensive survey of the number of mentally retarded in a community has even been undertaken using satisfactory techniques for identification. The most common figure cited, one based on expert opinion, is 3 percent of the total population. In actual practice, the figure has never been reached for an unselected segment of the population in any study where rigorous criteria of mental retardation were employed." [85] This figure has been used by the majority of states in the nation in their mental retardation planning programs; however, California, for one, does not feel that its use is warranted. "The Study Commission has been unable to find evidence to support so large a total (3%). Reliable information based on field studies is much needed but in terms of the Commission's aims and criteria, it seems realistic at this time to work with an estimated total, for the mentally retarded of California, of about 400,000, or 1.86 percent of the State's population, in 1970." [86]

In a review of the literature on prevalence of mental retardation which included studies from 1963, the New Jersey Division of Mental Retardation found estimates varying from .68 percent of the total population to 8.83 percent.[87] The lowest estimates of the number of mentally retarded persons—1 percent or less—are probably accurate estimates of the number of persons who are organically damaged and perhaps genetically inferior. A percentage of these persons suffer from what are at present uncontrollable accidents. The 8 percent estimate includes this 1 percent figure plus many poor people who are pseudo-retarded—people who seem retarded but are really victims of environmental deprivation. Beyond the 8 percent, however, there are many poor people who possess characteristics of retardation but who are not evaluated as mentally retarded.

The 8 percent figure also does not include those poor people who score slightly higher than their poor counterparts on intelligence and psychological tests but who never realize their full intellectual potential to the same degree as children from the middle class. Many of these persons can be found in the statistics of those rejected for military service because of inadequate mental development. The United States Office of Labor Statistics reported recently that "Of young men called up for draft examinations, the two Harlem areas had a 1964 rejection rate of 52 percent. Bedford-Stuyvesant had a rate of 47 percent." [88] A large proportion of these rejectees consists of those who have failed a simple mental examination. It was reported in 1962 that 56 percent of Negroes—many of them poor—who took the Armed Forces mental test failed. "The rate of failure for Negroes was twice as much in the Southern states as in the Northern and Western States, suggesting social, educational, and economic advantages in the latter area." [89]

The poor child who drops out of high school may be considered to be more talented than the poor child who is branded as mentally retarded while still in grammar school; but because of the brutalizing effect of poverty it would be impossible to support this conclusion objectively. Some poor people are more "fortunate" than other poor people— their good fortune need not be related to their inherent intellectual ability.

In any event, the difference between the performance of these children of poverty means little to the more "fortunate" poor child who is able to reach the level of a high-school dropout. At a time when even a high school diploma is lightly regarded by a society which demands sophisticated technical skills, the dropout's chances of escaping poverty are limited. Certainly, "to be poor is to be in danger of becoming retarded," [90] but beyond this is the fact that even for those who avoid the danger of retardation, there is still the almost unavoidable danger of remaining poor.

The costs of maintaining hospitals and providing services for the retarded—when added to the lost resource of the production of the employable person who is retarded, poor or both—are catastrophic. Though research suggests that the 3 percent figure seriously underestimates the extent of this national disaster, even this figure provides an indication of the scope of the problem. "Mental retardation affects nearly 6 million Americans. It affects 10 times more persons than diabetes; 20 times more than tuberculosis; 600 times more than polio. A retarded child is born every five minutes, 126,000 every year." [91]

Two facts emerge from these alarming statistics. Both have been verified by a number of investigators including Lemkau, *et al.*, Wishik, Levinson and the Onondaga study.[92] First, the prevalence of mental retardation is highest during the school years and especially for children in the ten-to-fourteen-year-old range. Second, the school more than any other institution determines who is and who is not mentally retarded.

The conventional interpretation of the first is that the school system, in contrast to any other public institution, makes demands on the child which are beyond his capabilities. The child, so the reasoning goes, is able to succeed initially, but then is unable to compete with his more talented peers. Very few commentators on the subject disagree markedly with this point of view. The comment of Burton Blatt, however, is most courageous and insightful: "It appears that only when this individual classified as mentally retarded but educable is of school age is he diagnosed as mentally subnormal; it appears almost as if the schools predestine the child to mental subnormalcy." [93]

The thesis of this book is that the supposed mental retardation of many of the poor is not mental retardation at all but environmental deprivation, which includes being "served" by institutions that do not perform in the way the public believes they do. The public education system, in particular, is not meeting its responsibilities; other institutions, including the state departments of welfare and health, are also failing. It appears that on many occasions we are not measuring mental retardation but our society's callousness toward the poor.

The Question, Who Are the Mentally Retarded?

Admittedly the field of mental retardation is beset by technical problems. No two researchers use the same techniques or criteria in their investigations, which helps to explain why the conclusions and results are so contradictory. In spite of these procedural difficulties, however, almost all studies of mental retardation indicate that Negro Americans are over-represented. These studies include the Delaware survey of 1963, the Onondaga County study, the reports of the Eugenics program in North Carolina and surveys of social characteristics and ethnic backgrounds of students in Special Education programs in Arkansas, New Jersey, Chicago and Milwaukee.[94] The same surveys indicate that people of low socio-economic status are also over-represented.

Unless one adheres to the racist theory that American Negroes are inherently inferior, a more suitable explanation must be found for the predominance of Negroes in these surveys. Certainly one reason is that Negroes are physically deprived to a greater degree than children from other ethnic groups because of inferior housing, health care and other factors relating to poverty. The great majority of the American Negroes and the poor, however, have no organic damage; rather they fail to live up to middle-class demands because they are grossly deprived. Due to the statistical chaos that characterizes mental retardation research, it is impossible to say with accuracy what the ratio is between those who suffer from organic damage and those who do not, but there are probably eight poor, deprived people—including Negroes—who are not organically damaged to every person who is. The encouraging results that have been publicized indicating the possibility of remedying cultural and general environmental deprivation substantiate this contention. L. M. Dunn states that "there are no known causes for over 90 percent of the mentally retarded individuals in the United States and Canada today . . . there are no discernible neurological impairments for 99 percent of the IQ 50–75 group." [95]

The mildly retarded represent an estimated five million persons or 89 percent of all the mentally retarded.[96] Of course there are also individuals with IQ's of fifty or below who are not neurologically impaired, but the percentage of such individuals decreases as the IQ level decreases.

The most frightening instance of the over-representation of the Negro among the mentally retarded is found in the reports of the Eugenics Board of North Carolina. Over a period of thirty-seven years this Board has overseen the sterilization of 6,851 persons,[97] some by means of castration.[98] Not all of these individuals were sterilized for feeblemindedness; mental illness and, until recently, epilepsy were also considered adequate reasons to subject individuals to this utter degradation.[99]

In the two-year period beginning July 1, 1964, 356 persons were sterilized: 124 were white, 228 were Negro, and four were Indian.[100] In the previous two-year period, 507 persons were sterilized: 150 were white, 323 were Negro, and fourteen were Indian.[101] There are approximately three whites to every Negro in the North Carolina population.[102]

The Eugenics Board claims that the majority of its sterilization cases were voluntary. The fact is, however, that "the majority of the persons sterilized were adolescents or young adults." [103] In view of their age and in view of the fact that these were individuals considered by the Board to be retarded, it is difficult to see how the decision to sterilize could have been entirely voluntary. The Board even admits that the written consent of the patient is not required—only that of the spouse or nearest relative.[104] In actual practice, it is the county welfare boards—apparently preferring sterilization to birth control or the solving of social problems—who submit most of the applications for sterilization.

The continuing use of sterilization is particularly tragic because the Eugenics Board itself recognizes that during the last twenty-five years "the increased knowledge in the field of mental health has revealed many causative factors for mental illness and mental retardation," of which hereditary factors are only a few.[105] The Board recognizes, too, that "birth control has made sterilization of noninstitutional persons less pressing." [106] Nevertheless, the need to destroy the reproductive potential of human beings, especially Negroes, does remain pressing. The implication that sterilization is still the only answer for institutionalized persons demonstrates the Board's absolute and frightening inability to recognize that it is the very institutional environment which makes these persons appear to be so incurably retarded. Possibly some of these unfortunate individuals— even those who have the misfortune to be black, institutionalized or both—do not join with the Board in "expressing its appreciation to the professional persons and to the general public who have contributed to the success of the program." [107]

Studies also indicate that the Negro is placed in Special Education classes to a greater degree than Negro population figures would warrant. This is the case in both Arkansas and New Jersey. A study completed by the New Jersey Division of Mental Retardation indicates very significant correlations between the indices of poverty, ethnicity and Special Education placement. The eleven school districts sampled were Bridgeton, Burlington, Elizabeth, Passaic, Camden, Montclair, Franklin Township in Somerset County, Perth Amboy, Englewood, Bloomfield and Fairlawn. Special Education attendance was correlated positively with seven factors:

% Earning less than $3,000	.74
Median income	.62
Estimated effective buying power per capita	.71
Estimated effective buying power per household	.64
% Unemployed in civilian labor force	.74
Median school years	.54
% Nonwhite	.42 [108]

The .42 correlation with nonwhite attendance is significant in itself; however, it is probable that this figure would be considerably higher if a study was conducted on a statewide basis and included such large urban areas as Newark, Jersey City, Paterson, Atlantic City and others.

The great preponderance of poor children in the public Special Education system, black and white, is nothing less than institutional ghettoization. The stigma of mental retardation added to low status places a child in a social and economic position that absolutely precludes advancement into the middle class. To be of low socio-economic status is to be in a less advantageous position than the middle-class child; but to be branded as mentally retarded is the last blow to the poor child's spirit. As Gladwin and Sarason state:

Although we know very little about the nature and magnitude of this impact [the emotional impact upon a child in his formative years of being segregated because of mental subnormality], it must be substantial, particularly in the areas of motivation for initiative and ambition which are so vital to occupational and social success in our society. No amount of intelligent dedication on the part of teachers of special classes can erase the fact that their pupils have been declared unfit to participate with their peers in an activity which society inflexibly demands of all its members of a certain age.[109]

Even more eloquent is the expression given to the problem by a child who was placed not in a Special Education class but merely a group for slow learners: " 'It really don't have to be the tests, but after the tests, there shouldn't be no separation for the classes. Because, as I say again, I felt good when I was with my class, but when they went and separated us—that changed us. That changed our ideas, our thinking, the way we thought about each other and turned us to enemies toward each other—because they said I was dumb and they were smart.' " [110]

How great then the impact of separation is for the child who is placed among the retarded. Once self-image and confidence are undermined, even extraordinary opportunities presented to the child are irrelevant for him; the child is simply unable to take advantage of them. The stigma of mental retardation is the brand of continued failure and the guarantee of the perpetuation of poverty.

The Misplacement of the Poor in Institutions for the Mentally Retarded

Numerous studies indicate that great numbers of individuals, usually people of low socio-economic status or from an ethnic or racial minority, are unjustifiably confined in institutions for the mentally retarded. These studies are particularly frightening because only the most severe cases of mental retardation should be institutionalized and only after they have undergone the most thorough evaluation.

Gibson and Butler in Ontario, Canada, investigated case records of individuals who had been admitted to an institution over a ten-year period. Those files which indicated organic dysfunction were separated from the others. The records which suggested that the patient suffered from an impoverished home life or was of foreign parentage were also separated.

In reviewing these records Butler and Gibson were surprised to find that where there was an identifiable organic difficulty, race and home environment were statistically comparable to that of the surrounding community. Where no such organic problem was indicated, however, Butler's review revealed that a much higher percentage of patients had come from depressed environments than of persons in the surrounding area or persons who had foreign-born parents. Ethnic background and socio-economic status became a priority criteria for placement in this institution.[111] Environment certainly had depressed individual performance, but faulty diagnosis by hospital officials completed the tragedy.

A second study of misplacement was conducted by Shotwell in the Pacific State Hospital, California. She theorized that institutionalization of Mexican-Americans might be erroneously determined on the basis of their verbal difficulties with a foreign language. Thus, she administered a nonverbal type performance test, the Arthur Performance Scales, to eighty American and eighty Mexican-American patients of comparable IQs ranging from fifty to seventy-nine. Again the results indicated gross misplacement.

The Mexican-American subjects gained an average of

twenty-two points on the Arthur scale, while the Americans raised their scores an average of only five points. Twenty-two percent of the American patients registered scores more than five points below their Binet scores, while no Mexican child showed this great a loss. Twenty-seven percent of the Mexican subjects had scores on the Arthur test which were thirty points higher than their Binet scores.[112] The obvious conclusion is that a great majority, perhaps all, of the Mexican patients should not have been institutionalized.

Another study at the Pacific State Hospital, this one conducted by Edgerton, provides additional insight into the inadequate diagnostic procedures used to admit patients into mental retardation hospitals and the seeming indifference of hospital officials concerning who is admitted and why. For a one-year period Edgerton and members of his staff observed the behavior of patients in the hospital and defined one group of patients as being "elite." Edgerton's analysis was focused on this group of individuals, who identified with one another, often congregated together and held mores which contrasted markedly with those of other inmates. The elite group was made up almost entirely of low socio-economic status people, and approximately 90 percent of them were American Negroes or Mexican-Americans.[113]

Robert Edgerton's comments on the complexity of the behavior and the interrelationships of the elite group are most interesting.

> Looking either at individual members of the elite or at their collective beliefs and behaviors, it is difficult, if not impossible, to discriminate between them and what we would reasonably expect from "normal" non-institutionalized persons of comparable age, socioeconomic status, ethnicity and experience. That persons whose IQ's average 55 are capable of conducting social relations of this complexity in an appropriate and ostensibly "normal" manner raises fundamental ques-

tions about the relationship between whatever it is that IQ tests measure and behavioral competence and appropriateness in everyday life.[114]

These studies also spotlight a problem of the definition of mental retardation as it relates to individual behavior. If mental retardation means that an individual is less talented than the normal person, then the mentally retarded person should perform less competently than others in the average social situation. Often this does not occur. As noted, the Onondaga study and reports by Lemkau, *et al.*, and Wishik indicate that after sixteen years of age—the termination point for mandatory attendance in the public schools—mentally retarded individuals are difficult to identify. The explanation of this striking fact provides additional corroboration for the thesis that people who are judged to be mentally retarded on many occasions are not so.

The questions constantly reappear. What is it that the mental retardation specialists are measuring? Why do Negroes fill the Special Education classes in New Jersey? Why are more Negroes being sterilized in North Carolina than whites? A study of the prevalence of mental retardation in Delaware, 1957, by Jastak and Whiteman suggests, although this point is not made by the authors, that once again diagnosticians do not discriminate between those people who are normal and those who are not. The poor and people from minority groups suffer more than anybody else from this astounding failure:

> One cannot help but be struck by the many similarities between the retarded and the non-retarded in many areas of adjustment. The lower degree of intelligence of the retarded group does not prevent a sizeable number of them from working gainfully, with a good deal of stability and satisfaction. Marital adjustment reveals no gross signs of disharmony. The retarded do not impose a disproportionate load upon community resources either in the form of legal

infractions or excessive demands for social service. They are distinguishable from the non-retarded mainly by their dissatisfaction with educational experiences, by their absence from formal social participation, and by their dependence in choosing leisure time activities.

Mental subnormality, as it appears, need not connote an inability to fill an acceptable social role.[115]

II.

Poverty and Organic Impairment

THE DEADENING INFLUENCE of poverty on mental ability begins at the moment of conception. This is especially unfortunate, for damage done to the child by his environment during the reproductive cycle is liable to be permanent, because organic, in nature. If this happens, no amount of good will or good environment later will ever erase the flaw in intellectual potential which is the birthmark of poverty.

Of course, not all the poor suffer demonstrable organic damage to the point of mental retardation. For the most part, in fact, the great majority of those retarded persons who are also poor are retarded for some apparent reason other than organic damage to the brain—a fact that serves to comfort a society that prefers to delude itself with myths about "genetic" inferiority rather than to provide all its members with equal life chances. But if the term mental retardation means anything, it means a failure to realize fully the intellectual potential inherent in every person at the time of his conception. If, then, as a result of inferior life chances, a person comes to function subnormally when his initial potential equaled that of his fellows, has he perhaps not suffered enough neurological vitiation during the reproductive cycle to produce, usually not demonstrable damage, but lifelong dullness?

This point is raised in order to show how wide-ranging the bio-medical effects of poverty may be; the chief concern of this chapter, however, is to show how poverty increases the probability that organic damage to the child's brain will occur during the perinatal period (the period from conception through the twenty-eighth day after birth). Consideration will also be given to those environmental hazards of infancy and early youth that predispose poor children to organic damage. The various—and relatively rare—clinical entities that also cause retardation and are known to be genetically transmitted will not receive attention, since these occur without relation to social class status.

Throughout this chapter the point of orientation, for which considerable clinical evidence now exists, is that "all men are conceived equal" [1] in intellectual potential, and that all observable differences in intellectual ability are the result of prenatal damage, the birth process, or postnatal (including cultural) conditions.[2] Or, to put it in sharper focus: "There is a great deal of information presently available to support the view that the range of normal human intellectual potential is much narrower than has been thought. The proportion of the population with innate intellectual potential below the range of normal is indeed small, and the majority if not all of these cases appear to be due to organic damage of the brain." [3]

Although it may be granted that all men begin equal in intellectual potential, it is also the case that the chance to continue on equal terms at least until birth is one the poor often do not have. Apart from the greater bio-medical risks a poor child will encounter *before* birth, he comes up against the cumulative ill effects poverty has had upon his female parent. As the result of such factors as her own lifelong poor health care, poor nutrition and poor education, the expectant mother is usually herself a very poor reproductive risk.[4] She is often ignorant of the basic facts of reproduction and contraception, and has access neither to the birth control devices nor to the legal and other abortive practices readily available to middle-class women.[5]

The poor woman is doubly disadvantaged in her prospects for timely and successful motherhood. On the one hand, she is more likely than her middle-class counterpart to be very young when she has her first pregnancy;[6] on the other, she is also more likely to have a greater number of children, and to go on bearing children until a later age, than the middle-class woman.[7] These conditions of low socio-economic status are significant because a high positive correlation exists between each of them and the incidence of prematurity, mental deficiency and gross maldevelopment.[8] Although prematurity, as a precondition of mental impairment, will be dealt with more fully later, it is important to note here that "in the premature infant, mental retardation is ten times more likely to occur than in the full-term infant." [9]

Similarly, it is necessary to consider the effect of failed abortion and pre-existing maternal disease in causing organic damage among poor children. Who knows how many poor women, lacking the financial and social advantages of their counterparts in the middle class, are led by desperation over illegitimacy and enormous families to resort to folk remedies or mechanical intervention on their own part, the failure of which permanently injures the child? Although, of course, no reliable statistics on this point exist, one may assume the number of such cases to be significant, if only by inference from the estimated number of *successful* abortions performed annually in this country.[10] In this regard, Masland reports on a follow-up study of forty-six cases of threatened abortion due to "disorders" early in pregnancy: "of these, 19 percent subsequently aborted. Of those whose pregnancy was complete, the incidence of prematurity, obstetrical death, and antepartum hemorrhage was three times as great as in a normal control group. The babies were in general small, and there was an increased incidence of abnormalities." [11] Pre-existing maternal diseases also present greater reproductive dangers to the poor; a New York City study, for example, showed the incidence of infectious syphilis in poverty areas to be six and one-half times as high as in good residential areas.[12] Similar correlations exist between poverty and other pre-existing maternal diseases that may lead to infant death or organic damage,[13] but at this point it is enough to understand that, as Masland notes, "It is certain that in many instances abortion or prematurity is the result of actual disease or injury to the fetus." [14]

It is instructive to examine the relation between low socio-economic status and both fetal mortality and prematurity. As with abortion, the assumption here is that the rate of fetal death in this country offers by inference a significant comment on the quality of reproduction enjoyed by those who manage to survive. On the other hand, the question whether prematurity causes mental retardation, or whether the reproductive problems that cause the prematurity also cause the retardation, is here quite irrelevant: the important point is that a close association exists both between prematurity and retardation,[15] and between poverty and prematurity. The central role of prematurity in relation to mental retardation becomes even clearer when one realizes that this phenomenon is also "the most frequently recurring factor now involved in infant death and morbidity." [16]

Fetal mortality refers to deaths that occur during the re-productive cycle, resulting either in abortion or in stillbirth. Obviously, accurate statistics are hard to come by, but re-searchers estimate the fetal death rate in the United States to be "150 or even 200 per 1,000 pregnancies, for urban, mar-ried, white women, and even higher for unmarried and for nonwhite women." [17] Although, again, causal connection between the factors of fetal death and the factors of poverty is difficult to establish with full certainty, it is clear that in many instances they are identical. "Instability of income," for example, "means higher rates of fetal loss." [18] Very young women and older women have similar high rates, as do those who have many pregnancies and those whose preg-nancies follow closely one upon the other—all of which ac-curately mirrors the poor woman's childbearing pattern. Statistics on rates of fetal death among the poor and the other classes also obscure differences in the real causes of such deaths, since those for the higher classes disproportion-ately reflect their advantages of better medical record-keeping and readier access to therapeutic abortion. [19]

Fetal mortality, prematurity and its most serious conse-quence, infant mortality, all vary inversely with socio-economic status. Rider, *et al.*, working in Baltimore in 1950–1951, found that among whites alone 7.6 percent of all births in the lowest socio-economic tenth were premature, as compared with 5 percent of those in the highest tenth. The overall rate for whites was 6.8 percent, with the lower tenths heavily over-represented. The rate for nonwhites, computed separately because of their much lower overall socio-economic status, was 11.4 percent of all births. [20]

For the entire country in 1952, the prematurity rate for whites was 7 percent of all births, and for nonwhites 11.2 percent—rates that compare closely with those for Balti-more during the immediately preceding period. [21] Although the national rates were not broken down by socio-economic status, their gross similarity to the city's rates offers the like-lihood that they followed the same class pattern. The overall prematurity rate for the Netherlands in 1952 was 3.5 per-cent.[22]

Progress in recent years toward reducing the occurrence of prematurity has not been very impressive. In Chicago in 1961, for example, the rate for all mothers living in the two lowest socio-economic areas was 14.1 percent.[23] Again, in New York City in 1964, the rate for all mothers living in four poor housing areas was 14.9 percent.[24] During 1965 the rate at Newark City Hospital, which serves the poor, was 16.5 percent.[25]

National statistics on infant mortality as related to low socio-economic status are equally revealing. (Infant mortal-ity refers to deaths that occur in the first year of life of in-fants judged to be alive at birth.) In the United States in 1964, the overall rate of infant mortality was 24.8 per one thousand births.[26] This figure in itself provides a significant comment on the quality of reproduction in this country, since fourteen other countries had lower rates than the United States in 1965—the best being Sweden with a rate of 12.4 per one thousand.[27] But when the figure is broken down by color, one finds that the mortality rate for non-white infants in the United States in 1964 was 41.1 per one thousand, or nearly twice the white infant rate of 21.6 per one thousand.[28] The nonwhite infant mortality rate is a good indicator of the relation between poverty and infant mortality in general, because in 1962–1963 in this country 72 percent of all families with annual income under two thousand dollars, and 80 percent of all families with annual income under four thousand dollars, were nonwhite. By contrast, in the same period 96 percent of all families with income over seven thousand dollars were white.[29]

In 1962 the *entire* city of Newark had an infant mortal-ity rate of 41.3 per one thousand live births, as compared with a statewide rate of 23.9 and a national rate of 25.3. The lowest city rate in New Jersey during that year was 13.9 per one thousand, which, if it had applied in the city of Newark, would have meant saving the lives of nearly three hundred infants.[30]

An infant born prematurely is sixteen times more likely to die during the neonatal period (first twenty-eight days of life) than one whose birthweight is normal.[31] If the premature infant does survive, he is, as has been observed, ten times more likely to become mentally retarded than is his full-term counterpart.[32] On the evidence available, for the premature infant both his chance to survive and his chance to avoid retardation are considerably better if his mother is not poor.

Thus, in the United States in 1964, the neonatal death rate for white infants was 16.2 per one thousand. But for nonwhite infants, whose families' socio-economic disadvantage has already been noted, the rate was 26.5.[33] In the same year in Newark—a city shot through with poverty— the neonatal death rate was 30.9 per one thousand.[34] Even the rate of 16.2 for white infants should offer this country little comfort, however, for between 1850 and 1899, despite all the advances in medical care since that time, the neonatal death rate of the children of Europe's ruling houses was only 12 per one thousand.[35]

Thus, it has also been demonstrated in a 1961 study that "while the performance of premature infants as a whole was poorer than that of full-term controls, socio-economic and cultural factors as determined by 'grade of mother' also played a role: the premature children at the lower social levels performed more poorly than those in the more privileged groups." [36] The report of the President's Panel on Mental Retardation, drawing upon a study of the development of premature infants conducted by Johns Hopkins University, offers the following related findings:

26.3 percent of those infants with a birth weight of 1,500 grams (3.3 pounds) or less have neurological abnormalities of sufficient degree to cause serious concern about their future development, while comparable figures for the remainder of the premature infants in the sample and for the full-term control groups are 8.2 percent and 1.6 percent, respectively.

Corresponding figures relating to minimum cerebral damage, believed to be the precursor of subsequent learning and behavioral difficulties, are 22.8 percent, 16 percent, and 10 percent, respectively.

17.6 percent of the smallest prematures have defective intellectual functioning.

Premature infants have 2 or 3 times as many physical defects and 50 percent more illnesses than full-term infants.

Prematurity generally has a deleterious effect, and 50 percent of these infants have handicaps ranging from minimum neurological damage to severe mental deficiencies and blindness.[37]

The relation between poverty and prematurity becomes still clearer when one realizes that "the prematurity rate varies directly with the percent of women who receive little or no prenatal care." [38] An extensive study done in New York City showed that women whose first prenatal-care visit took place during the first three months of pregnancy had a prematurity rate of 7.8 percent, which compares closely with the overall national rate for recent years. But among women who received no prenatal care, the prematurity rate rose to 20.3 percent of all births.[39] Similarly, in the District of Columbia in the early sixties the prematurity rate was 10.4 percent among women who had at least some prenatal care, but rose to 22.7 percent among those who received no care.[40]

It is usually not middle-class mothers, of course, "who receive little or no prenatal care." In fact, more than one-third of all mothers in U. S. cities over 100,000 population are now considered medically indigent[41]—that is, dependent upon public largess for any maternity care they may receive. Among the eight million women, or 12.1 percent of the nation's female population over age fourteen, who visited either obstetricians or gynecologists during 1963, the poor were grossly under-represented. Only 3.5 percent of women over fourteen from families with annual income under two thousand dollars, and 8.1 percent of women over fourteen from families with annual income under four thousand dollars, made such visits. By contrast, 17.1 percent of women over fourteen from families with income over seven thousand dollars were able to afford proper private care.[42]

When a woman needs prenatal care but cannot pay for it privately, her alternatives are to visit a public antepartum clinic or not to get care at all. Thus, in 1964 in New York City, 40.9 percent of all mothers living in four poor housing areas had late or no prenatal care, as compared with 12.3 percent of all mothers living in four good housing areas.[43] At the charity hospital serving the poor of Atlanta, Georgia, some 70 percent of all mothers in 1962 had late or no prenatal care,[44] while at Newark City Hospital in the same year one-third of all maternity patients had received no prenatal care at all.[45] In New Jersey in 1964 only thirty-three mothers per one thousand live births received medical clinic services through the aid of the Federal-State Maternity and Infant Care Program, a rate of service that met perhaps one-tenth of the actual need.[46]

The natural corollary of this lack of prenatal care among the poor is that they cannot afford private maternity care, and so give birth in general service delivery clinics or, too often, even without a physician in attendance. Evidence of the prevalence of these alternatives is readily available. For example, one may assume that if the poor cannot afford health insurance they will also be unable to afford private delivery service. On this basis one finds for 1963 that, of all delivery or surgical cases performed in this country, no part of the bill was paid by health insurance in 72 percent of cases involving families with annual income under two thousand dollars, nor in 52 percent of cases involving families with annual income under four thousand dollars. When the family income was over seven thousand dollars, however, nearly 80 percent of all such cases had part or all of the bill paid by health insurance.[47]

In New York City in 1960, 40 percent of all births were general service deliveries,[48] while in the District of Columbia in the previous year the rate of general service delivery was 60 percent.[49] A study of housing areas in New York City in 1964 found that nearly 80 percent of all births to women living in four poor housing areas were general service deliveries.[50]

More than 10 percent of all nonwhite mothers in this country in 1964 gave birth without a physician in attendance; this rate was more than 20 percent in several Southern states.[51] But even in the city of Newark, where midwives are hard to find these days, there were 110 unattended births in 1965.[52]

In general service delivery clinics, as in all forms of mass production, quantity must of necessity take precedence over quality. This observation should not be misunderstood as meaning that clinic service is tantamount to no service at all, but the quality of medical service one receives is directly related to the price one pays. For general service delivery the poor pay very little or nothing and, thus, they "definitely get second-rate medical care. This is self-evident to anyone who has worked either with them or in public medical facilities." [53]

The same question about quality—and the organic effects the lack of it may have upon the child—arises with respect to prenatal care as dispensed in public clinics. The former director of the Newark Maternity and Infant Care Project writes of the barriers thrown up in the path of poor women seeking publicly sponsored service: "It was not difficult to see why one-third of the Newark City patients elected to risk delivery without prenatal care in preference to clinic attendance; the reason was not primarily indifference to health needs. A description of registration and clinic procedures there followed blow by blow the complete listing of 'Deterrents to Prenatal Care.' " [54]

As to the quality of prenatal care actually received by those poor women who elect to overcome the barriers, the chairman of the Department of Obstetrics and Gynecology at Emory University Medical School observes that "In these charity hospitals, the massiveness of the antepartum clinics is unbelievable. It is simply not possible to give adequate antepartum care under these circumstances of too many patients; too few doctors, nurses, social workers, and others; and inadequate facilities." [55]

Perhaps, though, the most fitting comment on this subject was made by Mrs. Sargent Shriver when she said that in this country "pregnant cows are getting better care than pregnant women." [56] As the result of this situation and other forms of social indifference, the United States has a much higher incidence of mental retardation than countries like England, Denmark and Sweden,[57] where adequate national maternal and child care services help ensure that poor women and their children will at least be treated as equal to farm animals.

Although it is not the purpose of this chapter to examine the bio-medical etiology of organic mental retardation, some causal factors are so clearly related to poverty as to require specific consideration. Organic damage due to disease and poor nutrition, for example, both during the reproductive cycle and after the child is born, occurs among the poor much more often than among the other classes, largely because the poor get more diseases and less—or worse— food than the others. Other environmental hazards of poverty which predispose children to organic damage, while these also exist to some degree for the other classes, exist for the poor to so great a degree that the accident is perhaps not that they suffer the damage, but that they escape it. Because these factors relate to organic damage so directly, then, they will be discussed here. Other evidence of the health hazards of being poor, and the inadequacies of the social institutions set up to provide the poor with health care, will be given in a later chapter.

Diseases or related conditions that may cause or increase the risk of mental retardation in children fall into two groups: those that occur during the mother's pregnancy, and those that occur after the child is born. The former affect principally the mother and thus often, by extension, the fetus; the latter affect the child directly.

Examples of the first group are syphilis, toxoplasmosis, rubella, salivary gland virus, vaccina[58] and various maternal infections of the urinary tract and malfunctions of the reproductive system.[59] It is not proposed here to demonstrate associations between poverty and each of these conditions, but simply to note that the general association between poverty and poor health, as the chapter on that subject will make clear, is so well documented by now as to be unquestionable.[60] What is important here, however, is to understand that pregnant poor women, who have the greatest need for good prenatal care, get very little. "They have a high incidence of anemia, malnutrition, chronic vascular disease, toxemia, contracted pelves, premature labor and other problems"[61]—all of which, in view of the sort of treatment they are likely to receive, ensure that their children stand a considerably greater risk of suffering organic damage than do those of the other classes.

The second group—the diseases of infancy and childhood—likewise put the poor children at greater risk of suffering organic damage. Nonwhites have death rates, for example, up to or more than twice those of whites for the following diseases: meningitis, measles, encephalitis, diphtheria, whooping cough, scarlet fever, nephritis, influenza and pneumonia.[62] Many of these, if not promptly and properly treated, leave their mark upon the survivors in the form of permanent damage to the central nervous system, the apparatus of intelligence.

But do the children of the poor, white and nonwhite, get prompt and proper treatment? In 1963, twelve and one-half million children, or 20 percent of all children under age fifteen in this country, visited a pediatrician one or more times. Nearly 30 percent of all children under fifteen from families with annual income over seven thousand dollars made such visits. But only 12.8 percent of those whose families had income under four thousand dollars, and 9.6 percent of those whose families had income under two thousand dollars, were afforded proper private care.[63]

For those who cannot afford private care, there are of course public postpartum clinics, and there is also no reason to think that the quality of service in them differs in any respect from that dispensed in the public antepartum clinics already discussed. It is also noteworthy that in New Jersey —where over a million persons are living below the poverty line—only forty-five children per one thousand received service in 1964 at publicly sponsored Well-Child Conferences.[64]

Like poverty and disease, poverty and poor nutrition are closely associated. What is often not realized, however, is that poor nutrition and mental retardation are also associated, sometimes in a causal relationship. The aim here will be to show how poor nutrition, whether during the reproductive cycle or after birth, can impair intelligence, sometimes by causing permanent organic damage to the central nervous system.*

An abstract of William J. Culley's work on nutrition and mental retardation offers a useful overview of medical research findings:

> The nutritional aspects of mental retardation were reviewed. Two main categories were used: (1) nutritional deficiencies that cause mental retardation; and (2) nutritional problems associated with mental retardation. Some findings in the first category included: (1) caloric deficiency contributes to prematurity and greater incidence of mental retardation; (2) protein deficiency in pregnancy produces lower birth rates and less vitality in newborns; (3) a vitamin E deficient diet in pregnant rats causes encephaly in many of the young; (4) neuritis in animals is caused by a deficiency of thiamin (vitamin B1); (5) riboflavin (vitamin B2) deficiency in pregnant rats can cause CNS malformations (i.e., hydrocephalus); (6) niacin deficiency causes personality changes resembling psychoses and apathy; and (7) hydrocephaly has been produced in young whose mothers were on vitamin B12 deficient diets. The problems that would occur in the second category usually were due to motor disturbances in children leading to difficulty in chewing and swallowing food.[65]

As discussed earlier, the effects of lifelong malnutrition and other disadvantages often make the poor woman a poor reproductive risk. These carry over into her period of pregnancy, and thus reinforce the ill effects that poor nutrition

---

* It will be taken for granted that the poor get less or lower-quality food than the other classes; the grounds for this assumption will be demonstrated, and the full extent of malnutrition in this country portrayed, in a later chapter on food-assistance programs.

during that period has upon the fetus. Several studies have shown how malnutrition during the reproductive cycle can impair the life chances and in particular the intelligence of children.

John D. Tompkins reported on 750 consecutive patients who were given "advice and vitamins" during pregnancy and who subsequently had *no* premature infants.[66] Dieckmann studied the dietary habits of many pregnant women in Chicago and reported that "A strikingly significant correlation was found between the condition of 302 babies rated by the pediatrician and the average protein intake of the mothers. The percentage of excellent babies steadily increased with increasing intake of protein. So large a value could occur by accident only about one in 10,000 times." [67]

One research team divided a group of 404 pregnant poor women into five subgroups according to their protein intakes, and found that "The lowest birth weight, low vitality and large number of deaths in the newborn infants occurred among those born to the most poorly nourished mothers. The incidence of prematurity rose sharply with the decrease in the nutritional status of the mother." [68] Lastly, and entirely to the point, Harrell, *et al.,* in a study of twenty-four hundred pregnant poor women, found that vitamin supplementation during the last half of pregnancy "does increase the intelligence of their offspring, at least for the first four years of their lives" [69]—at which time cultural deprivation sets in, as the chapter on that subject will demonstrate.

Two other studies, one on children and one on rats, show how poor nutrition after birth also impairs intelligence, perhaps permanently. Stoch and Smythe, working in England, reported that malnourished infants have lower average intelligence later in life than do adequately nourished infants, and offered the "obvious suggestion that severe poor nutrition could retard intellectual development." [70] In this country, Culley, whose earlier findings on nutrition were given previously, found recently that malnutrition during infancy causes permanent organic damage in the adult brain of rats. As he observes: "It does not seem unreasonable that malnutrition very early in life of humans might very well reduce the total number of brain cells as it did in the rats. . . . Other research already has shown that severe undernourishment early in life causes retardation." [71]

A special form of organic damage, related both to poor nutrition and to the environmental hazards of poverty, should be discussed at this point. This is lead poisoning, the result of eating chips of lead-based paint, which in turn often results in permanent mental retardation. Its usual victims are poor children between the ages of one and six, since it is mainly the poor who live in the sort of housing where such paint is still a danger. It is also poor children who most often develop pica, the craving for unnatural food substances—thought to be connected with inadequate nutrition —that leads them to eat paint and other noxious matter.[72] The lead poisoning of children in the decaying cities of America is largely unacknowledged or ignored. The medical director of the New York Health Department's Poison Control Center, Dr. Joseph Cimino, estimates that in New York alone there are 25,000 children so afflicted.[73]

Poor children risk organic damage in various other ways also, none of them perhaps as far-reaching in their ill effects as disease or malnutrition, but all of them equally dangerous to the individual child.

Poor prenatal care, overwork, undernourishment and the other physical stresses and emotional frustrations of the culture of poverty[74] cause higher rates of fetal death among poor women, and more complications (for example, prematurity) than among women with adequate income. The generally unfortunate circumstances under which these same poor women actually give birth also make it more likely that their offspring, if so far unscathed, will by accident or professional inattention suffer the brain injuries possible when delivery is difficult or precipitous.

Even if born healthy, a poor child does not stand a great chance of growing up physically unscathed by the hazards of their environment. Kenneth B. Clark, in his study of Harlem, one of the heartlands of Poor America, describes the risks a child encounters while living there:

> The multiple use of toilet and water facilities, inadequate heating and ventilation, and crowded sleeping quarters increase the rate of acute respiratory infections and infectious childhood diseases. Poor facilities for the storage of food and inadequate washing facilities cause enteritis and skin and digestive disease. Crowded, poorly equipped kitchens, poor electrical connections, and badly lighted and unstable stairs increase the rate of home accidents and fires. Nor is the street any safer. Harlem's fourteen parks, playgrounds, and recreational areas are inadequate and ugly, and many of the children play in the streets where heavy truck traffic flows through the community all day. Far more children and young adults are killed by cars in Harlem than in the rest of the city.[75]

These dangers, often resulting in brain injury and thus crippling the child's intellectual development,[76] are bad enough when they occur "by accident" during delivery or in the home and in the streets. Yet they almost seem inconsequential—not statistically, perhaps, but morally—when the very persons upon whom the child must depend for protection from the threatening world around him, his parents and family, have themselves been so brutalized by that world that they become the source of the injury. This "battered-child syndrome," [77] as the textbooks call it, is better caught in the words of a woman whose childhood experience of it has led her to adopt a subtler approach in dealing with her own children: "When I beat them I do it in the normal way, with a strap or whatever is handy, but I never," as her mother often did, "cut them or break their heads." [78]

ཏ III.

The Effects of Cultural Deprivation on Intellectual Performance

RECENT LITERATURE, in both education and mental retardation journals, concerned with the causes of low academic performance and with mental subnormality, has been characterized by a liberal use of the concept of "cultural deprivation." This should be fortunate because it provides a link between research in education and mental retardation; however, this link has seldom been appreciated even though educators and workers in the field of mental retardation have been discussing the same problems.

Some confusion is generated by the use of the concept of "cultural deprivation," however, because it is often used interchangeably with such ill-defined terms as "disadvantaged" and "underprivileged," which have appeared in a number of different contexts. It is clear that almost 100 percent of the poor are culturally deprived. However, it is just as clear that not all the poor are mentally retarded. The relationship between cultural deprivation and mental retardation needs to be clarified.

Poor, culturally deprived children comprise the majority of the retarded. Mental retardation, as has been noted, is a major source of the loss of human resources in the nation. But even the staggering statistics on retardation do not indicate the extent of this loss. These statistics do not include the millions of children who are not quite mentally retarded but who never come close to realizing their native intellectual potential.

Frank Riessman estimates that in 1950 one out of every ten children in the fourteen largest cities in America was culturally deprived. Because of continued migration to the cities, states Riessman, this figure had risen to one in three by 1960 and by 1970 it is likely to be one in two.[1] Taking into consideration the fact that one-sixth of the population of the nation is living in these fourteen cities; that between 1940 and 1950 80 percent of the national population growth was centered in these cities and that between 1950 and 1967 this percentage increased to 97 percent, the overwhelming immensity and urgency of this problem is only too evident.[2]

Life within the dark, inaccessible cell of poverty is as multifaceted and complex as behavior in any other social environment. It is practically impossible to describe adequately the particular environmental factors that impinge upon human growth and initiate human pathology.

Two facts are eminently clear, however. First, the environment of the cell of poverty is the cause of pseudo-mental retardation (apparent retardation but really "environmental deprivation"). Second, to eradicate this type of retardation it will be necessary to attack every aspect of poverty. Contrary to the mode of thinking illustrated by medical research, no spectacular breakthrough can be made until the whole structure of the culture of poverty is destroyed, a structure which includes substandard housing, underemployment and unemployment, inferior education, inadequate health services, poor nutrition and discrimination. Each facet of poverty overlies the other in the etiology of pseudo-mental retardation. No amount of research will ameliorate the conditions and human suffering of poverty as long as poverty itself remains. Research, in fact, can reveal only the obvious, for as long as civilization has existed man has known that severe poverty degrades and debilitates man. We do not need a more sophisticated, academic understanding of the exact way poverty breaks the human spirit. We need to eliminate poverty.

As emphasized earlier, the major obstacles to the social change that would eliminate mental retardation are prejudice and ignorance of the real nature of poverty. This prejudice and ignorance are reflected by the fact that the very terms used to describe the interaction between the poor man and his environment perpetuate misunderstanding. The term "cultural deprivation" is a euphemism. It suggests that the only difference between the poor child and his wealthier counterpart is a trip to a museum or a zoo, and it masks more fundamental aspects of an impoverished existence. A label is never a satisfactory replacement for an in-depth, comprehensive understanding of a particular phenomenon; but in the case of poverty and subsequent pseudo-mental retardation a label is especially inadequate. The brutality of poverty cannot be communicated in language, except, perhaps, in great literature.

In America, the family is responsible for the acculturation and intellectual stimulation of the child. The process of family interaction is vital to the child's growth and to his ability to benefit later from the educational experiences offered in school. "The family is the first and most basic institution in our society for developing the child's potential, in all its many aspects: emotional, intellectual, moral and spiritual, as well as physical and social. Other influences do not even enter the child's life until after the first highly formative years." [3] The process of family life among the poor, which, in hundreds of thousands of families, is solely an accommodation to low socio-economic status, helps explain the higher prevalence of pseudo-mental retardation.

The household is the complete world of the child for a long period of time, and the quality of life in that world is crucial. If the child is not stimulated adequately in all his senses from birth, his intellectual potential will wither. As J. McV. Hunt indicates in discussing Piaget's theories of child development:

> . . . the rate of development is in substantial part, . . . a function of environmental circumstances. Change in circumstances is required to force the accommodative modifications of schemata that constitute development. Thus, the greater the variety of situations to which the child must accommodate his behavioral structures, the more differentiated and mobile they become. Thus, the more new things a child has seen and the more he has heard, the more things he is interested in seeing and hearing. Moreover, the more variation in reality with which he has coped, the greater is his capacity for coping.[4]

Or as I. N. Berlin, head of the Division of Child Psychiatry, University of Washington, states in a more informal way, "Every infant needs certain experiences with sensory stimuli so that physical and psychological development and the accompanying curiosity, investigativeness, and learning can take place. Among disadvantaged youngsters, the lack of sensory stimuli is an important factor in their learning difficulties." [5]

The single most important human relationship is that between the mother and her child. But financial difficulties in poor families often interfere with that relationship. Because the poor male cannot earn enough to support the family, the mother often is forced to go to work herself. Indeed she often finds it easier to find employment than does the male because of the large number of jobs open in such fields as domestic work. The result is that a greater percentage of poor women work than do women from other social classes; the children are left at home under the supervision of the older children, or they are left to take care of themselves. The middle-class working mother is able to provide an adequate surrogate to care for her children.

Even when the poor mother is at home, everyday pressures of poverty destroy the mother-child relationship. Usually there are more children to attend to, which means that less attention can be given to each of them. "The underprivileged home is a crowded, busy, active, noisy place where no one child is focused upon. There are too many children for this, and the parents have too little time." [6]

Moreover the practical demands made on the mother of low socio-economic status severely reduce the chances of a middle-class mother-child relationship. The ill effects of manipulating a budget that cannot possibly meet the needs of her family, of attempting to clean a home where the plaster is falling from the ceiling and roaches are embedded in the walls, and of many other difficulties, take their toll in human energy and spirit. These are problems that do not have to be dealt with by middle-class mothers. The very attention directed toward these chores is diverted from the child and impedes his intellectual growth. "The answer for the child's failure to learn usually lies in the mother-child relationship. The mother has so little for herself that she has little to give her youngsters. Barely able to manage, surrounded by children, with little companionship except from those who are similarly deprived, she is overwhelmed by hopelessness and helplessness." [7]

The poor, through ignorance and the inability to pay for contraceptive devices, often have large families. This they characteristically attribute to fate. There is no other alternative. However, the relationship between the size of the poor family and low IQ is not the hereditary matter that some have believed it to be. As Hunt indicates, it "is mainly a function of the amount of time that is available for parent-child interaction." [8] Furthermore, as Thomas F. Pettigrew states, "the negative relationship between family size and intelligence does not appear among wealthy families who can afford to provide stimulating attention for each child." [9] Thus, the rearing style necessitated by poverty works against the poor child's chances of developing in a normal fashion. "Often the infant does not experience any consistent and persistent warmth and nurturance. He may not be talked to very much; his beginning babbling may not be encouraged by his mother's playful imitation, and for long periods of time he may not be played with or loved much. His discoveries and achievements are not sources of delight and pleasure to his depressed and overburdened mother." [10]

It should be noted that the absence of the father in the family is a factor in explaining the general depression of intellect and higher prevalence of pseudo-mental retardation among the poor. The presence of the father is helpful to the normal intellectual development of the child. Martin Deutsch and Bert Brown have stated that "Children from homes where fathers are present have significantly higher IQ scores than children in homes without fathers." [11] As Daniel Moynihan has emphasized, the statistics on Negro families headed by females are alarming: "Almost one-fourth of Negro families are headed by females. . . . The percent of nonwhite families headed by a female is more than double the percent for whites. Fatherless nonwhite families increased by a sixth between 1950 and 1960, but held constant for white families. It has been estimated that only a minority of Negro children reach the age of 18 having lived all their lives with both parents." [12]

It should be added that fatherlessness is only one variable in an extremely complex environment; its significance should not be overemphasized.

In general, the person-to-person interaction that takes place in poor families damages rather than enhances the potentialities of the infant. Beyond the absence of individual attention for each child, a psychological environment develops which is extremely unhealthy. It is characterized by the misunderstanding and the unhappiness that is the very stuff of poverty. "The negative side of the underprivileged family is easy to see: the family may be prematurely broken by divorce, desertion and death; the home is overcrowded, the housing facilities inadequate; considerable economic insecurity prevails; both parents frequently work, and thus the children may be neglected; and typically the irritable, tired parents use physical punishment in order to maintain discipline." [13]

The effects of this kind of life in a very few years reach the core of the child's personality. One cannot accurately measure these effects for several years; however, the legacy of poverty probably impairs the child's development before three years of age. An example of the effect of racism on a child is provided by Kenneth Clark:

> Many Negroes live sporadically in a world of fantasy, and fantasy takes different forms at different ages. In childhood the delusion is a simple one—the child may pretend that he is really white. When Negro children as young as three years old are shown white and Negro appearing dolls are asked to color pictures of children to look like themselves, many of them tend to reject the dark-skinned dolls as "dirty" and "bad" or to color the picture of themselves a light color or a bizarre shade like purple. But the fantasy is not complete, for when asked to identify which doll is like themselves, some

Negro children, particularly in the North, will refuse, burst into tears, and run away.[14]

The impoverished white child has his own particular burdens to bear. As Oscar Lewis has said, "The individual who grows up in this slum culture has a strong feeling of fatalism, helplessness, dependence and inferiority. . . . Other traits include a high incidence of weak ego structure, orality and confusion of sexual identification, all reflecting maternal deprivation; a strong present-time orientation with relatively little disposition to defer gratification and plan for the future, and a high tolerance for psychological pathology of all kinds." [15]

The obstacles to the intellectual development of the poor child are found outside as well as inside the family. Many of these obstacles relate to his contacts with middle-class society. These contacts not only fail to spark a healthier recognition of self than is made possible by life in a ghetto family, but also, they actually leave the family—with all of its inadequacies—as the child's only refuge from a hostile world.

> Slum people know that they have little ability to protect themselves and to force recognition of their abstract rights. They know that they are looked down on and scape-goated. They are always vulnerable to the slights, insults, and indifference of the white and Negro functionaries with whom they deal—policemen, social workers, school teachers, landlords, employers, retailers, janitors. To come into contact with others carries the constant danger of moral attack and insult.[16]

The intellectual differences between a poor child and a middle-class child are not only caused by differences in the relative stability of their respective households. It is generally understood, although it has not been publicized, that there is a "hidden curriculum" in the middle-class family which virtually guarantees that the child will be more ready to begin school than his poor counterpart. The middle-class child is intensively tutored by his parents, especially his mother, and his rate of intellectual maturation is therefore quicker. This training program was a part of the middle-class parents' own rearing pattern; because of the rewards and reinforcement they received from it, they pass the same training on to their children.

The success of the parents in properly educating their children, however, is dependent upon more factors than their own educational and social background, their love for their children and the time they are able to allocate to interact with them. A suitable physical environment is needed for the training of children; it is difficult for satisfactory education to take place in a slum home.

The most widely recognized and most frequently tested aspect of what psychologists call "general intelligence" is verbal ability. It is a dimension of intelligence which supposedly has significance for all other cognitive elements. In the home of the poor family, where typically too many people reside in too few rooms, the noise level usually is unbearable. There is no quiet for the urban slum child even when the noise has subsided in one's own flat, for "the family of the poor lives cheek and jowl with other families of the poor. The sounds of all the quarreling and fights of every other family are always present if there happens to be a moment of peace in one household. The radio and television choices of the rest of the block are regularly in evidence." [17] For the infant this constant din is noxious and unintelligible. In order to survive the child must deaden his mind to the stimulus of sound. The situation is an ideal one for a child to learn inattention.[18]

Implications of this inattention are numerous and serious. The impoverished child does not develop the ability to discriminate between sounds or to learn which sound is associated with which object or phenomenon. An example given by Charles Silberman illustrates this problem graphically: "he [the poor child] fails to develop an ability to distinguish between relevant and irrelevant sounds, and to screen out the irrelevant. If, for example, a truck rumbles by while the teacher is talking, the lower-class youngster hears only one big jumble of sound; the middle-class child has the ability to screen out the irrelevant noise of the truck and listen only to the teacher." [19]

Because of the inferior education that poor people receive, the quality of language in the home differs greatly from that of middle-class people; this, too, contributes to the underdevelopment of the impoverished child. L. Aserlind evaluated the speech and language patterns of low socioeconomic status mothers and their children and found that in terms of mean sentence length, complexity of vocabulary and structure of syntax, both mother and child were retarded in language development. [20]

In the middle-class family a mother may say to her child, "Joseph, go to the shelf and bring me the blue bottle of ink." The lower-class mother in the same situation probably says "get that," or "bring it here," or even just points to the article she wants and by use of sign language, communicates her desires to the child. The poor child often has a poor language model to emulate.

More important, perhaps, than the quality of language in an impoverished home is the inability of the poor parent to interact with the child in a way that is productive for language development. Middle-class parents often correct the grammar, syntax and style of the child's speech. In the poor family the infant quickly develops a language capability equal to that of the parent and is unable to progress beyond that point in the face of the obstacles of home life. The child inherits a limited and distorted vocabulary, an abbreviated syntactical model and a style of language that is often completely unintelligible in the formal world of school.

Tragically, even the most earnest and devoted mother can merely transmit to her child a language capability as inadequate for the child as it has been for her. "The mother who is present and does reinforce verbal behavior by her children would be reinforcing, in many cases, an inadequate production or a response not generally used in the verbal community at large. Her own impoverished verbal repertoire would be a serious limitation on the development of her children's behavior." [21]

In the most severely impoverished environments the parents actively suppress the verbalization of the growing infant. The pressure of children's noise in very cramped quarters added to the personal irritation of general failure are so great that often the child is silenced. "The next one that speaks, they goes through that wall." [22] This problem is made abundantly clear by the poor mother herself:

> Where living conditions are crowded and a mother must continually care for five young children by herself under rather adverse financial circumstances, the children's vocalizations probably are noxious events for the mother—events which she tries to terminate. She then makes punishment the usual consequence of the child's speech behavior, and, thus suppresses it. . . . Aversive stimulation such as physical injury and loud, sudden screams is probably administered as a consequence of the child's speech. This procedure probably limits substantially the child's speech and language development in the early years. [23]

Constant suppression reveals itself in the poor child's behavior even at the kindergarten level; he does not understand much of what is said to him. Words make no sense. And this liability is even greater, in that the average person hears only 60 to 80 percent of what is said to him. The remainder must be pieced together through the use of syntax models—models the poor child is deprived of: "Collins (1964) compared the linguistic skills of culturally advantaged and disadvantaged kindergarten children and reported that the ability to garner meaning from auditory stimuli was the least developed of all linguistic skills among the disadvantaged, while the advantaged group achieved its higher scores in this all-important skill." [24]

The language capability of the middle-class child in school is also determined by the efficient role that the parents play as a source of information. The parent serves as a guide as the child tests the reality of his world and reaches out to comprehend new knowledge. Much of this information is directly related to the all-important future experience in the public-school classroom.

The impoverished parent is bereft of the very information and the techniques of gaining knowledge that are essential for the child's academic success. Because the parents are scholastic failures themselves—and know it—and because they have generally failed in the middle-class world, they frequently defend themselves by perpetuating the ignorance of their progeny. The poor child often grows up without an awareness of the existence of books, pictures, magazines, three of the basic elements of school life. Nor does the child develop the ability to use these materials as the middle-class child does.

> The last ones they want to admit it (illiteracy and ignorance) to are their own kids because already they've got trouble maintaining status with the kids. The kids may go to school. The parents may be out of work and look like failures anyway. The kids are full of questions the parents can't answer. So the first thing the parents do is make sure there's no printed material in the house, no newspapers or magazines or even comic books, because the kids might ask the parents something about it.[25]

Language development of the poor child is further impeded by the paucity of objects in the home. The child cannot identify that which he has not encountered. The middle-class home, in contrast, is replete with the appurtenances of modern society, such as furniture of different styles and shapes, lamps, curtains, bookshelves, rugs and perhaps an electric can opener or an electric toothbrush. The homes of the poor are frequently barren of all of these objects. Orange crates serve as tables and the floor is the child's bed. The inside of the Johnson home as reported by Ben Bagdikian in a Chicago slum is not even as meager as many:

> To this psychological estrangement between the poor and comfortable is added the differences in common household experiences. This may extend . . . to the more common alienation from those pieces of hardware that are part of the total American culture. This is the world of the vacuum cleaner, the dial telephone; the younger children would regard the circular arrangement of numbers and letters as a mystery. . . . Yet such mechanical fixtures are part of the vocabulary and concepts of the young, and school books and intelligence tests. The Johnson children have never seen a movie and since a donated television set broke some time ago have lost even that touch with the outer world.[26]

The impoverished environment of the poor child extends beyond the house in which he lives. Rarely, however, does he get away from a twenty-five-block area around his neighborhood. More important, the child's forays into the outside world do not include those experiences which stimulate the language ability of middle-class children in so many ways. The zoos, museums, art galleries, libraries and airports are as unknown and unexplored for the poor child as is Mars for people on earth.

The overall effect of language impoverishment is profound. The child comes to kindergarten unprepared to profit from the school experience. He often does not know that objects have names such as wall, book, chair, or table. He may be equally ignorant of the fact that an object can be identified in terms of more than one property, such as a ball, which is red, round and bounces. His experience with language may have been so meager that he does not know his own age, address, or even his own name.

Simply stated, millions of poor children at the first-grade level are inattentive, unable to understand formal, spoken English, and are unable to speak. These children are well on their way to being classified as mentally retarded. Warren Cutts, the reading specialist of the U. S. Office of Education, illustrated the vocabulary deficiencies of the culturally deprived child:

> Hugh? . . . unh-huhh . . . nuttin . . . naw . . . wuh? . . . 'cuz . . . unh-unh . . . sho!
>
> Is this a readiness-for-reading vocabulary? Definitely not! Yet, unfortunately, these "words," with variations for emphasis and inflection—plus a few other one-word sentences and a generous sprinkling of vulgarities—comprise the speaking vocabulary of many culturally disadvantaged first graders. These and other strange noises that take the place of standard American English reflect the impoverished language background of these children.[27]

In a middle-class home the child's curiosity is encouraged and rewarded. Just the opposite occurs in the disadvantaged home. Early in life when the infant begins to crawl, his explorations are curtailed, for there are too many people and not enough room; his growth must be subjugated to the needs of others. As the child grows older and begins to question his parents, this activity is also suppressed because, as has been suggested, the adult doesn't have the information that the child desires.

The poor child thus suffers not only from a paucity of information about the world of words and labels, but the very spirit of intellectual curiosity is significantly stunted, and the child does not learn how to use questions, an all-important intellectual tool. "In the child's formulation of concepts of the world, the ability to formulate questions is an essential step in data gathering. If questions are not encouraged or if they are not responded to, this is a function which does not mature." [28]

The inadequacy of the role played by disadvantaged parents contributes to the underdevelopment of another function of the intellect—namely, memory. The concept of time and the relationship among different types of experience are not phenomena which the child becomes aware of automatically. Indeed, these factors, as anthropologists have noted, are not common features of all societies. The poor child is not acculturated properly to the nuances of our society's understanding of these concepts. Without concerted guidance of the type that takes place unconsciously in the middle-class family, the disadvantaged child remains oriented to the present. He does not comprehend the other dimensions of time and experience. "It is adults who link the past and the present by calling to mind prior shared experiences. The combination of the constriction in the use of language and in shared activity results, for the lower class child, in much less stimulation of the early memory function . . . there is a tendency for these children to be proportionately more present oriented and less aware of past-present sequences than the middle-class child." [29]

It is not appropriate to dwell too long on the environmental factors that depress intellectual development; however, a number of additional factors must be considered. The physical surroundings of the slum home inhibit the growth of the visual and tactile senses of the child. As noted, the sparsity of physical objects in the home contributes to the language deficiency of the disadvantaged child; additionally, however, the objects which are present are unvaried and repetitious in form and color[30] and deter the growth of visual discrimination and acuity as well. Propensities in the field of spacial relations, which are so important in drawing and in pictorial expression, never mature. As Deutsch has stated, "The sparsity of objects and lack of diversity of home artifacts which are available and meaningful to the child . . . gives the child few opportunities to manipulate and organize the visual properties of his environment and thus perceptually to organize and discriminate the nuances of that environment." [31]

The same drabness of physical objects contributes to the understimulation of the tactile senses. While a poor child may have an old toy and perhaps a broken doll to play with, he does not have the opportunity to manipulate a number of different objects of different sizes and configurations. The impoverishment is not solely a function of not having blocks or toys, however; often the poor do not even have the cooking utensils or other household articles which could serve the same purpose. J. McV. Hunt aptly describes the impact of this general deprivation on the growth of a child: "With few things to play with and little room to play in, the lower-class home offers little opportunity for the kinds of environmental encounters required to keep a two-year-old youngster developing at all, and certainly not at an optimal rate." [32]

A very intimate relationship exists between the stultification of the child's intellectual development and his psychological maturation and well-being. Because the impoverished child does not prosper and does not develop the intellectual equipment needed to function effectively in our society, because he remains embedded in a whole subculture of misfortune, his psychological orientation becomes gnarled and unhealthy. Psychological health is based largely upon a positive self-image, which in turn depends to a major degree on one's ability to control one's environment and thus one's fate. And this is exactly the potentiality that remains undeveloped in the ghetto: "In most societies, as children grow and are formed by their elders into suitable members of the society they gain increasingly a sense of competence and ability to master the behavioral environment their particular world presents. But in . . . slum culture growing up involves an ever-increasing appreciation of one's shortcomings, of the impossibility of finding a self-sufficient and gratifying way of life." [33] Poverty begets incompetence—and incompetence guarantees that the cycle of poverty will continue on.

Another cause of the apparent retardation of the poor is inadequate nutrition. That poor diet causes depressed intellectual performance was recognized centuries ago; in modern times the lethargy, dullness and pseudo-mental retardation of many poor children can be ascribed to this same factor.

Anyone who has ever gone without food can appreciate the pernicious effects that hunger has on concentration and alertness. Unfortunately, as will be discussed in detail later, the understanding of the relationship between hunger and pseudo-mental retardation has not moved our government and society to insure that children in the United States are well fed.

In the educational world the revelation that poor diet is the cause of subnormal academic performance is revived from time to time. Miriam Hughes, director of the National School Lunch Program for New Jersey, indicated recently that "teachers of students who were benefiting from the Pilot Project Breakfast Program were astounded at the alertness of children who were previously apathetic and listless." [34] Nevertheless, thousands of children in New Jersey come to school hungry, and leave in the same condition. The intervening period of "education" is a blur of physical and psychological yearning for the food they do not receive.

A study conducted by R. F. Harrell indicates that if an

expectant mother suffers from an inadequate diet, it can depress the intelligence of her unborn child. An experimental group of low socio-economic status mothers was supplied with vitamin supplements during the last half of pregnancy. Three years later, an analysis of intelligence scores of the children born compared to those of a control group indicated a five-point IQ differential in favor of those whose mothers had received the vitamins. This gap increased to eight IQ points in the following year.[35]

A study conducted by Mavis Stoch in South Africa corroborates the importance of proper diet for intellectual development. An experimental group of children who "were the most grossly undernourished Cape Coloured children that we could find" were matched against children in somewhat better circumstances, although they, too, were probably not receiving all the nutrition they needed. After a period of several years the control group was tested at IQ 76.7, and the experimental children scored an average of 15.5 IQ points below this mark.[36] The thesis was sustained once again: if a child does not eat enough nutritious food, he will not develop to his full intellectual capacity.

Along with nutritional deprivation—and often as a result of it—the poor child suffers from other health problems which also serve to limit his chances of academic success. These problems will be considered at greater length in subsequent sections of the paper, but it is important, in the present context, to bear in mind the dimensions of this situation. Lola Irelan notes:

> Rates of degenerative diseases, particularly, cardiovascular disorders, vary with socio-economic conditions. Rheumatic fever, for example, is rare among the well-to-do, but its incidence rises as one looks down the social scale. The chronic diseases (e.g. heart disease, diabetes mellitus) are relatively more prevalent among the poor. Incidence of all forms of cancer is inversely related to income. Cervical cancer occurs

more often and causes more deaths among women of the lowest classes. It has been found that premature births are more frequent among lower class mothers. Infant mortality is strongly associated with both low income and low occupational status. Class status is also persistently associated with prevalence of schizophrenia. A similar association has been documented for other diseases.[37]

For the majority of poor children the ill effects of poverty do not lead to a complete psychological or physical breakdown. While they clearly show the signs of strain from their impoverished surroundings, the children's condition is not serious enough to require hospitalization, institutionalization or even special education. But if one looks for these children, they can be found. Green, *et al.*, comments about the condition of children in a particular elementary classroom: "many are disturbed, seven severely. Fifteen or more have asthmatic attacks. Ten thumbsuckers. Any diversion, as little as change of subject—everybody in back stands up and starts talking." [38] The "minor" physical illness and emotional disturbance of impoverished elementary school children become the diseases and psychoses of adulthood.

It is another measure of our society's indifference to the plight of the poor that only recently have investigators begun to realize that we have been confining mentally ill people rather than mentally retarded individuals. Obviously a prescription of therapy would be different depending upon which disorder is to be treated: "Mental retardates, as a group, appear to have a higher incidence of behavioral disturbance than individuals in the general population. These disturbances seem to occur in mental retardates for the same reasons that they occur in persons of normal intelligence . . . many individuals labelled as mental retardate are primarily emotionally disturbed, and . . . retardation is a function of or develops from, emotional disturbances." [39]

The poor, then, carry more than the burden of their

everyday suffering. They not only have to fight to survive in the slum but they must, additionally, bear the callous indifference of the larger society. Even their illnesses, which are part of their adaptation to misery, are misinterpreted or overlooked by that society. "The slum, with its vibrant, dense life hammers away at the individual. And because of the sheer, grinding, dirty experience of being poor, the personality, the spirit, is impaired. It is as if human beings dilapidate along with the tenements in which they live." [40] The final insult is that the poor are treated to irrelevant therapy in an institution after they have collapsed emotionally.

IV.

Public Education and Mental Retardation: The Self-Fulfilling Prophecy Fulfilled

Although the system of public education in America is certainly not solely responsible for the failure of the poor to learn and for their over-representation in Special Education classes for the mentally retarded, it is more responsible than any other single institution in our society. Martin Deutsch supports this view: "The responsibility for such large groups of children showing great scholastic retardation, the high dropout rate, and to some extent the delinquency problem, must rest with the failure of the schools to promote the proper acculturation of the children. Though some of the responsibility may be shared by the larger society, the school, as the institution of that society, offers the

only mechanism by which the job can be done." [1] Or as
Robert M. MacIver has declared: "The school's function is
to educate and where the family and the community fail to
promote the social adjustment and the psychological development necessary to prepare the young to receive the education the school offers, it must step in to provide it within
the area of its capacity." [2] Stated in a somewhat different
way, "When the home is a proportionately less effective so-
cializing force, the school must become a proportionately
more effective one." [3]

Some public school systems do educate impoverished
children, and they serve not only to illustrate what should be
done in many other school districts but also to emphasize
that poor children are not dullards who must be segregated.
Although no educator would suggest that all the knowledge
necessary to teach impoverished children has been found, or
that there has ever existed a school program which utilized
all the information we do have, the Demonstration School
project of 1957 in New York and the Banneker school system in St. Louis prove without question that poor children
can be educated just as well as children from any other
socio-economic class. The disadvantaged child will learn
properly, will have a normal or higher IQ and will enjoy
education, if the school has the resources to meet the child's
needs, wants to educate the child, and believes the child has
the potential to learn. The deficits of poverty can be overcome.

But the dismal academic record of impoverished children in the majority of public schools in America, despite
the human potential of these children and examples of their
academic success elsewhere, indicates that public schools
can be, and often are, a component of the culture of poverty. Joan Roberts has written: "Potential to learn is
affected not only by the culture in which the child is raised,
by the ethnic subculture to which he was born, by the socio-

economic position of his family in the social structure, by his earlier experience in learning activities; but also by the school and teachers who may, through inhibiting procedures, decrease the child's capacity to use his learning potential." [4] And the recent survey of education in America, the Coleman Report, states:

> For most minority groups, then, and most particularly the Negro, schools provide no opportunity at all for them to overcome this initial deficiency [cultural deprivation]; in fact they fall farther behind the white majority in the development of several skills which are critical to making a living and participating fully in modern society. Whatever may be the combination of nonschool factors—poverty, community attitudes, low educational level of parents—which put minority children at a disadvantage in verbal and nonverbal skills when they enter first grade, the fact is the schools have not overcome it.[5]

Instead of placing the blame for academic failure on the child, as is commonly done, the emphasis should be placed on the educational system, which fails to educate the child.

The statistics demonstrating the failure of the public school system to educate the poor completely outnumber the isolated examples of success. It is generally recognized that not even a high school diploma means that a person can read a daily newspaper or compute well enough to make small change. The following comment from a personnel director of a large corporation in Massachusetts reflects a nationwide situation: "We have been testing for about ten years. We give simple spelling and arithmetic tests to all the high school graduates who come in here, and frankly we are surprised at the number who can't pass. I'd like to give you the exact figure, but some time ago one of our men mentioned the high rate of failures and it raised such hob in the community that we decided it would be better if we kept them confidential." [6]

A study of the reading ability of welfare recipients in Chicago also illustrates this educational failure. Six hundred and eighty men and women on relief were given the new Sanford reading test. Of this group 6.6 percent were illiterate because they had not completed five years of formal education. In the remaining group, however, 50.7 percent also tested as functionally illiterate, even though many of these people had attended public schools for a considerable number of years. Four out of five who completed the fifth, sixth and seventh grades were functional illiterates; three out of eight who finished grammar school or higher also failed to indicate the ability to comprehend the most simple elements of formal education.[7] Commenting on this study, May states that the findings "are not unique to the second largest city in the United States. They could be duplicated in the urban areas of Los Angeles, Detroit, Pittsburgh, Cleveland, New York or Philadelphia,"[8] or in any urban area in New Jersey.

An anti-poverty endeavor in Detroit found equally distressing evidence of educational failure. It was noted that of twenty-two hundred employed or underemployed youth, 84 percent had graduated from high school. "Many could not read second-grade materials or solve seventh-grade arithmetic problems."[9]

Another study from Chicago indicates that 70 percent of four thousand high school dropouts, the majority of whom were of low socio-economic status, possessed normal or above-average IQ's.[10] Obviously, the system is not educating the very people whom educators believe have the potential to learn.

The sequence of student failure further suggests that the fault lies with the system rather than with the child. As Kenneth Clark suggests, "The farther these students progress in school, the larger the proportion who are retarded and the greater is the discrepancy between their achievements and the achievement of other children in the city. . . . This deterioration can be traced in sequence, beginning with the elementary schools and following through the junior high schools to the high schools." [11] In delineating scholastic retrogression in Harlem, the Haryou Report indicates that "22 per cent of the third grade students in that area were reading above grade level, while 30 per cent were reading below grade level. . . . By the sixth grade, 12 per cent were reading above grade level and 81 per cent were reading below level." [12] The same sequence was found for tests of arithmetic, word knowledge and general intelligence.[13]

In discussing the in-school deficits which develop in Harlem schools and become even wider over the early education years, the Haryou Report comments: "From this we can infer that the sources of educational problems of Harlem pupils lie in processes which occur during the time they are in school, rather than in processes prior to their entry into school." [14] Or as Susan B. Silverman concludes in her review of literature on education of the disadvantaged: "The fact that the achievement deficit of these children is cumulative and increases over time seems to reflect some basic weaknesses in both curriculum and school practices for these children." [15]

The process of academic retrogression is certainly not a phenomenon limited to a particular school system or region of the country. Statistics document its existence in virtually every major urban area. For example, in Boston: "As they [the culturally deprived] go through school they fall farther and farther behind the national average. The typical child in Boston has a reading achievement of 5.6 in the sixth grade [the national norm is 6.0] while the typical child in predominantly Negro districts reads at 5.1, almost a full year behind. By twelfth grade those discrepancies double." [16]

In Big City, an unidentified city of the Midwest, the Iowa Achievement Test—a nationally standardized test which purports to measure "skills" in language, work, arithmetic, reading and vocabulary—was given to all students. Patricia Sexton notes that at the fourth-grade level there is a 1.36 grade-level difference between students from the highest socio-economic class and the lowest. At the sixth grade this gap extends to 1.82 grade level and in eighth grade, "the lowest-income students are almost two years behind the highest-income students." [17]

And Charles Silberman comments, "the opportunity is being muffed: no city in the United States has even begun to face up to the problem involved in educating Negro—or for that matter, white slum youngsters." [18] For many the burden of educational inequality and mediocrity added to the strain of ghetto life is too much. They simply fail:

> Those who fail are shunted into classes for "children with mentally retarded development" and "opportunity" classes. Most stay in their regular classes that "meet their ability." . . . It is an ironic and tragic inversion of the purpose of education that Negro and white children in ghetto schools tend to lose ground in I.Q. as they proceed through the schools and to fall further and further behind the standard for their grade level in academic performance. The schools are presently damaging the children they exist to help.[19]

Russell Kirk comments specifically about the inability of the public school to teach reading: "The four million elementary school students which the National Council of Teachers of English estimates to be poor readers are poor readers not primarily because they are mentally or physically or emotionally defective or because they are Negroes or because their parents are ignorant and indigent; they are poor readers primarily because the textbooks and the methods of teaching reading are poor." [20]

Perhaps a final declaration of the inefficiency of the public education system to teach impoverished children is provided by Horace Mann Bond. He has noted that it takes

12,672 fathers who are professional and technical workers to produce one National Merit Scholar, while it takes 3,581,370 fathers who are laborers to produce one such scholar.[21]

Simply stated, the public education system in the United States was never designed to educate children in the way that our technological society now requires. For the purposes of this discussion, the history of education may be divided into two major periods. Until nearly the end of the nineteenth century, education was classical in nature. Its aim was not to educate the masses, but rather to train the offspring of the country's socio-economic elite to be professional and community leaders. The common man, with his more immediate material aims, was unlikely to stay long in what was clearly the exclusive preserve of the upper classes.

At the turn of the twentieth century, with the continuing waves of immigrants coming to this country, many saw the need for the public education system to acculturate the foreigners to the American way of life. "Social reformers saw the school as the only public agency able to Americanize the immigrants and lift them out of their squalor." [22] Under the threefold influence of the theories of John Dewey, the protests of social reformers, and the economic pressures emanating from businessmen who wanted an orderly, soberminded and prudent labor force, the curriculum of the public school was altered to include courses on health, vocational training and civic responsibilities.

Although intellectual discipline slackened considerably under these influences, the public education system played an effective role in the absorption of millions of foreign children in the American democratic system. Moreover, education was in no sense essential for financial prosperity. The rags-to-riches tale of the janitor boy rising to bank president was more glamorous and more real than a schoolboy getting a B.A. degree from college and going on for even higher education and a respected and powerful position in the community.

This brings us to the present. The educational system in operation today is a mixture of both the early classical period in American education and the later progressive period with its emphasis on life adjustment. It was never designed to educate all the children of our society to the needs of an atomic age. But this is not a recent or unadvised conclusion; cogent, intense and widespread criticism of the educational establishment had been heard even before Sputnik. Philip H. Coombs, former director of the Ford Foundation, has stated: "Almost everything that the schools and colleges are doing is obsolete and inadequate today. This applies to the curriculum, to the arrangements for teacher training, to textbooks, to organization, to methods of teaching and learning, to school architecture." [23] A report released on August 13, 1967, makes an indictment of the New York public school system that cannot be easily dismissed, and also has its implications for other systems.

> The New York City school system appears "paralyzed" by its problems and has failed to stem "a precipitous downhill trend," a federally sponsored study has found. A report on the study, made by a City University research team, charged that the system had not made any meaningful change in curriculum, administrative structure, general organization and teacher recruitment, appointment and training for at least three decades. Large, cumbersome and burdened by a congested bureaucracy, the school system has suffered from inertia or has responded dilatorily to the new major demands being made upon it.[24]

Before we isolate this and other reports, it is well to remember Silberman's comment on the New York school system: "And New York is probably doing more than any other large city; in most the picture is even worse." [25] Furthermore, we should refer to the statement of the U. S. Commissioner of Education, Harold Howe, at the Education Conference held at Rutgers University in 1966: "There are only two states in America that can deal with the U. S. Office of Education on equal terms and they are California and New York." [26]

The major reason for the inhospitability of the public schools to poor children is that impoverished parents have no influence over school policies. The organization and composition of the school board and the school insure that this occurs. As Goodwin Watson points out: "The American public school is a curious hybrid: it is managed by a school board drawn largely from upper-class circles; it is taught by teachers who come largely from middle-class backgrounds, and it is attended mainly by children from working-class homes." [27]

Power is the essential element in the political world of education; power is based on social importance, financial resources and knowledge of the political machinery and how to manipulate it—all these the poor do not have. Of course, pronouncements from educators insist that all parents are welcome to express their grievances, but it is no mischance that the poor person receives less consideration than others. And as the House Task Force on Education indicates in a discussion on parent reaction to low tracking of their children: "Parents, according to printed policy, have always had the right to protest the placement of their children in basic or regular track. Relatively few did, or do, however. Most parents of poverty area pupils would feel themselves incapable of arguing the point, even if they were aware of it." [28]

August Hollingshead, in *Elmtown's Youth*, provides a good example of the role of social and economic influence in the treatment given to a child by the school. It is presented here to suggest how other questions such as school organization, budgetary considerations and type of educational programs offered are resolved to the detriment of lower-class students.

In the course of his study Hollingshead noted that the school had set up new regulations for tardy students. Any student arriving late for school would have to stay after recess for one hour. When the rule was put into effect, the superintendent of schools stated confidentially, "You cannot make a rule like that stick in this town. There are students who simply cannot be sent to detention. Their families will not stand for it. I look for trouble from this."

Shortly thereafter, Frank Stone, Jr. (from the highest social class) parked his father's Cadillac in front of the school after the late bell had rung, leisurely closed the door, picked up his notebook and entered the school. He walked into the superintendent's office and casually mentioned, "I guess I'm late again." The superintendent, however, intervened on Stone's behalf and he was not sent to detention. This incident for all practical purposes ended uniform enforcement of the rule.

Approximately a month later a student named "Boney" Johnson (from the second lowest social class) entered the superintendent's office late to school. After belittling the student—"So my pretty boy is late again! I suppose it took half an hour to put on that clean shirt and grey tie! . . . . I suppose you took a bath last night, too"—the superintendent ordered "Boney" to go to detention.[29]

Professional educators have felt that the control of the educational apparatus was in the proper hands—namely, their own or those of other people of the same social class. Because school board positions are generally nonpaying positions and require a considerable amount of free time, many interest groups are not well represented.

In the Big City study, Patricia Sexton notes that the school board members were engaged in the following occupations:

2—housewives
1—advertising executive
1—executive of one of the largest corporations in Big City
1—owner of a steel company
1—owner of a medium-sized business
1—physician[30]

In a 1956 study of school boards in Illinois, it was found that representatives were largely of upper- and upper-middle-class groups, and while farm representation was diminishing, the influence of business was expanding.[31] Robert Havighurst indicates in a review of studies on this subject that about 75 percent of all board members are business proprietors, business managers, professional workers, or wives of such men, and that from 3 percent to 15 percent are manual workers.[32]

No school system in the nation is doing nearly enough to educate impoverished people to the necessity of involvement in school affairs, and to share influence over the educational process. It is, of course, true, as Sexton indicates, that disadvantaged parents "seldom seek out contact with the school, since they usually do not have enough confidence or know-how for this . . . They are not articulate or well educated; they are self-conscious about themselves and the way they dress, and they generally feel uncomfortable and out of place in school." [33]

But the educational prospects of disadvantaged children appear dim if the process of bringing poor parents back to the school is not begun. It is highly questionable that there can ever be true equal opportunity in education unless the voice of the poor parent has some authority. It is utopian to believe that a middle-class parent will ever insure that the disadvantaged child has the same chance to succeed as her own. Mothers will always believe that some children are more equal than others.

Because of the political and economic weakness of poor

people, among other reasons, the process and general philosophy of public education is damaging to the disadvantaged child. The orientation of the public school in and of itself disenfranchises the poor. It suggests that only the student can be held responsible for failure; the institution, because of its position and strength in society, is unassailable. The poor have to accept the academic fate of their children —failure—with resignation.

More than any other word, "fixity" characterizes the process of public education. This rigidity is more or less the same for all social classes, except that it does not interfere with the educational progress and the future economic success of the middle-class child as it does with the impoverished child. For a number of reasons the middle-class child is able to endure public education—the poor child cannot:

> Someone has said, and rightly so, that "too many of our schools are like tailors trying to fit the boy to the pants instead of the pants to the boy." A mass of evidence indicates that the boys and girls at the lower end of our income spectrum, struggling to keep up with unrealistic school tasks but steadily accumulating deficits in intellectual attainments, will leave at the first opportunity and join the ranks of that 30 percent labeled "drop outs" or, more appropriately, "push outs." [34]

The reward system of the school, which is so important in stimulating or depressing a child's motivation, is also rigidly structured in a way that unjustly penalizes the disadvantaged child. It is a pedagogical truism that positive reinforcement is generally preferable to punishment. In the classroom, however, it is the child of high socio-economic status who garners the reward of high grades. In Big City, for example, note the percentages of failures for each income group:

Percentage of Failures

Income Group	Social Studies	English
I lowest	14.6%	16.8%
II	13.9	10.9
III	12.7	9.3
IV	10.2	8.5
V	7.9	6.6 [35]

These facts suggest that poor children should not be placed in competition with others until they have fully adjusted to the school and are progressing satisfactorily. As Arthur Pearl has noted: "If the school continues to punish such children [disadvantaged] with failing grades and other forms of humiliation, these youngsters will be disaffected with the whole educational process. Even if they are not actually told they are stupid, the school implies it. They are asked to read when they can't read well; they have to stand at the board and face the laughter and ridicule of their friends. If they finally decide not to go to school, they are arrested as truants." [36]

Not only are disadvantaged children unfairly matched in competition for grades, their failure serves as a basis upon which the child is disenfranchised from other rewards and pleasures.

School grades are the chief means for rewarding students for achievement and good conduct. Poor grades served as negative judgments and, in the long run, often curtail pupils' future opportunities. Students who perform below a certain standard not only receive low grades, but also may be denied, as a direct consequence, a wide variety of privileges and opportunities within the school. They may lose esteem among the classmates, are seldom chosen for prestigious school assignments, and are often excluded from participation in certain extracurricular activities. . . . While poor grades may be an incentive for some students, they may create a double or triple penalty for others.[37]

The importance of school rewards is best appreciated through the feelings of a child. The attitudes expressed below are those of a child who, because he was in a low track, was denied participation in prestigious activities.

(What happened after you were separated?) (You said you didn't have any opportunities any more. What kind?) I mean —they'd get special things. When you're ready to graduate from junior high, you get to take pictures and go on picnics and stuff. Basic classes don't do this. You don't get to take any pictures in basic classes. You don't get a chance to be in the recital, you don't get the chance to do certain things. You know 9-7, 9-8, and 9-9, they used to give plays—they gave a big play. But none of the basic section was included, although we were classified as the ninth grade.[38]

One study of 705 students from six different communities supports the contention that the upper-class students get most of the rewards, such as good grades, citizenship prizes, social acceptance, school offices held and an opportunity to participate in extracurricular activities. A most important reinforcement of behavior—teacher acceptance— was also reported by Abrahamson as being accorded to the poor to a lesser degree than to children from other classes:

. . . According to the teachers themselves, there was a tendency to favor the students from higher social class backgrounds. The teacher indicated that the students of higher social class backgrounds were chosen more often for little favors—running errands, monitoring, committee chairman, and the like—than were other children. Obversely, when it came to handing out disciplinary measures there was a tendency for the students of lower social class backgrounds to receive more than their share according to the rating of the teachers.[39]

The middle-class child gets the rewards and the disadvantaged child gets the punishment.

Another obstacle to intellectual growth for disadvantaged children is de facto segregation. It is a sociological fact of life in urban America that the migration of the middle class to suburbia and the questionable geographic placement of schools have created a situation where the poor are lumped together in low socio-economic status school districts. This phenomenon is particularly damaging to the American Negro.

It is not that all Negro schools or school districts cannot compete successfully with other districts of a different ethnic make-up, but rather that at this time in history the separation of black and white students automatically implies the inferiority of the Negro and thus impedes intellectual growth. The implications of the Brown vs. the Board of Education decision are as valid today as they were in 1954:

> To separate them from others of similar age and qualifications solely because of their race generates a feeling of inferiority as to their status in the community that may affect their hearts and minds in a way unlikely ever to be undone. . . . A sense of inferiority affects the motivation of the child to learn. Segregation . . . has a tendency to retard the educational and mental development of Negro children and to deprive them of some of the benefits that they would receive in a racially integrated school system.[40]

The separation is the damaging influence; the question of race is central only in the Brown decision. It is unfortunate that the damage done when socio-economic segregation is allowed to take place is not more widely understood. As Robert Havighurst has commented: "While this statement [separate educational facilities are inherently unequal] was made with regard to race, the evidence on which it was made applies with great force to separate educational facilities on any basis where one group is regarded as superior and another group as inferior. Separation on the basis of socio-economic status is as much a separation of superior from inferior in the United States as is separation on the basis of skin color." [41] Specifically, "non-white lower income students do better when placed in mixed or middle-class schools." [42]

The grouping or tracking of children, a common practice in public schools, is a form of de facto segregation and evades the responsibility of teaching the poor. First of all, it is the poor child who is tracked and not children from other socio-economic classes. For example, the poor are not as "ready to read." Esther Milner indicates in a study of first-grade children that all children studied from the lower-lower class scored poorly on a reading-readiness test while *all* the children in the lower-upper and upper-middle class scored above average. [43]

Judge Skelly Wright, in his decision which declared tracking unconstitutional, noted that low tracking and low social and economic background go together. Moreover, "only a small percentage of students—not more than 10 to 15 per cent—move up a track each year. Very few are cross-tracked—permitted to take classes outside their track." [44] In Washington, D. C., the city that Judge Wright evaluated most closely, tracking begins in kindergarten and first grade: "Metropolitan [form R] reading readiness tests are given in kindergarten or first grade, and on the basis of these scores, pupils are sorted into 'ready to read' first grade groups or 'not ready' junior primary groups." [45] A school system which initiates tracking at such an early level in the child's academic life, and thus permanently mires the individual in an inferior educational program, fails to "take account of the psychological damage that can come from such an encounter between student and the school; and cannot be certain that the student's deficiencies are true, or are only apparent." [46]

The stamp of inferiority that is applied in a tracking program is not unnoticed by the children:

> Children themselves are not fooled by the various euphemisms educators use to disguise educational snobbery. From the earliest grades a child knows when he has been assigned to a level that is considered less than adequate. Whether letters, numbers, or dog or animal names are used to describe these groups, within days after these procedures are imposed the children know exactly what they mean. Those children who are relegated to the inferior groups suffer a sense of self-doubt and deep feelings of inferiority which stamp their entire attitude toward school and the learning process . . . they have a sense of personal humiliation and unworthiness.[47]

Wilson comments that tracking of disadvantaged students "comes to many of them as an unanticipated and discriminatory jolt." [48]

Lack of money directly affects the disadvantaged child's opportunity in the classroom. The inability of impoverished parents to buy new clothes and shoes means that the child will not even be able to dress as well or in the same fashion as the wealthier child. All children are conscious of material symbols of affluence and power and the lack of proper clothing certainly affects the wealthier child's attitude toward the impoverished child and affects negatively the poor child's attitude toward himself. As Robert and Helen Lynd have observed in the Middletown study:

> A number of mothers who said that a child had left school because he "didn't like it," finally explained with great reluctance, "We couldn't dress him like we'd ought to and he felt out of it," or, "The two boys and the oldest girl all quit because they hated Central High School . . . If you don't dress right you haven't any friends . . ." "My oldest girl stopped because we couldn't give her no money for the right kind of clothes. The boy begged and begged to go on through

high school, but his father wouldn't give him no help. Now
the youngest girl has left 10-B this year . . . she was too
proud to go to school unless she could have clothes like the
other girls." [49]

Neither the education system nor any other public institution takes this problem into account. No one, it seems, is
responsible for mitigating the plight of the impoverished
mother facing the "awful months":

"Here it's almost the end of the school year but already it
seems like the awful months."
The awful months?
"Yes. The awful months. August, December, March. August
you got to find clothes if the kids are going to school that
year. December you just have to find some money somehow
for Christmas presents. March is usually Easter and everyone else will have new clothes and you've got to try to find
some little bright and new item so the kids won't be ashamed
to go to church or to school." [50]

Extra money for dating, parties, transportation by taxi and
other such expenses is simply out of the question.
Perhaps the expenses mentioned so far can be characterized as "out-of-school costs." "In-school costs" indicate,
however, that the commonly held notion that public education is free is invalid. Sexton lists a number of the expenditures that are part of the "hidden price" of free public
education:

Some of the required and optional costs of keeping up were:
admission fees for athletic contests . . . dramatic performances, dues for student body, class or club memberships;
mechanical drawing, woodworking, laboratory-science and
other courses; charges for gym clothes, lockers, towels, do-
mestic-science uniforms, band and orchestra instruments
and uniforms, athletic equipment, rooters' caps, class sweat-
ers, rings, keys, pins; expenditures for various textbooks,

workbooks, pens, pencils, paper, ink; subscriptions to the school yearbook, newspaper, magazine, handbook, costs of photographs for the school yearbook and for graduation, graduation and announcements, diploma fees, commencement caps and gowns.[51]

Perhaps the most graphic example of the magnitude of these in-school costs (some of which were not even included in Sexton's list) and of our indifference to the effect that they have on the feelings of poor children and their ability to learn has been noted in another study: "In the Hunter project . . . We did a survey on one eighth grade class for a three-month period as to extra money children were asked to bring to school. It amounted to $26.50. In this class 70 per cent of the children were in families on the welfare rolls of New York City. A family on welfare in junior high school receives $0.25 a month extra for the child's extra expenses!" [52]

Moreover, it seems to be common procedure to charge fees for summer school. This practice completely ignores the financial difficulties of impoverished families. If a disadvantaged child is motivated to attend, the family will have not only to pay for the cost of the school but also to lose the money that the child will not be able to earn because he is attending school. "Another aspect of what some have come to call 'compensatory education' is free summer school. In many communities tradition restricts summer school only to those children who can afford it. Though the fee is small, it is sufficient to keep many depressed-area children from attending. And it is in these areas particularly that children frequently need to make up work, to improve their background, to secure enrichment." [53]

Books are important tools in education. If they are appealing to the child, they serve as a stimulus to explore other ideas written by other people; if the content of the books is uninteresting or, even worse, psychologically disturbing, it may permanently impair the child's interest in reading and education. "The earliest impressions develop attitudes that persist." [54] It is an indictment of education across the nation that educators have only rarely dealt with this problem.

It was not many years ago that some texts used in New Jersey schools were blatantly bigoted. One can only faintly imagine the severe discomfort that must have been suffered by a Negro child reading Gornman and Gerson's *Geography Primer*. One father comments on part of the effect that it had on his daughter:

> In her ninth year I found her standing in front of a mirror, staring at herself, squeezing her nose, and rubbing her cheek. She asked me, "Daddy, am I a Negro?" "What do you mean," I asked, to which she replied, "Teacher told me today that I'm a Negro, and a Negro, teacher said, is an ugly black person with thick lips, broad nose, and sloping forehead and a ring in his nose—a savage." "Well, where did teacher get such nonsense?" I asked. "From this book," she answered, producing Gornman and Gerson's *Geography Primer,* which was used in primary schools in Philadelphia, New York, New Jersey, and Delaware.[55]

Although no one knows if this kind of prejudice has been totally eliminated in public schools, it is true that the percentage of texts that are openly racist has diminished greatly. The replacements, however, are probably to the same degree "silent destroyers" of the intellectual potential of disadvantaged students, both colored and white. The newer texts used in public schools simply avoid dealing with any subject that is related to the impoverished background of the student receiving the education. These books suggest that poverty in America does not exist. That this frustrates and makes the impoverished child anxious is obvious.

One specific way the schools have unconsciously augmented feelings of alienation (among lower income students both black and white) is by introducing children to the world of reading and books through readers which hold up as an exclusive model a cultural pattern of the white middle class suburban family. The child knows in his heart that the school gives the highest prestige value to books, and yet everything that is familiar to him is excluded from the ways of life presented in the books which the schools provide.[56]

The content of current textbooks and other curricula material offers no orientation point for impoverished children because it does not include any of the experience, language, or pictures of a slum life. In its place they offer suburban utopia. In a study of fifteen commonly used readers in the country, Otto Klineberg indicates that

. . . Life in general is fun, filled almost exclusively with friendly, smiling people including gentle and understanding parents, doting grandparents, generous and cooperative neighbors, even warmhearted strangers . . . The life portrayed in these readers must represent a very frustrating experience for [poor children]. Are no other families as poor as ours? Does everybody else live in a pretty white house? Are there no crowded tenements except where we live? Are we the only ones who can't go out and buy the toys we want? [57]

The existence of minority-group children in public school readers is almost totally unacknowledged, and when reference is made to a person of another skin color or culture, he is pictured as a subordinate individual. The content of the readers suggests that "the American people are almost exclusively white or Caucasian. The only exception discovered in the fifteen readers refers to a visit to a Western ranch, near which lived an American Indian family, who spent most of their time 'making beautiful things . . . to sell to the white people who come to the Indian country.' " [58]

A study authorized by the California State Board of Education of 116 basic and supplementary books reinforces Klineberg's analysis: "The results are shocking. The illustrations are populated almost exclusively by Anglo-Saxons, and the texts rarely mentioned a minority group except in a traditional, stereotype situation. The Negro or Mexican-American student seldom sees a member of his own group depicted as an executive, professional or skilled worker." [59]

The almost absolute irrelevancy of the material presented in textbooks forces the disengagement of the poor child from the learning process. Textbooks are phony; life in the streets is real. Ultimately the phoniness of the text may force the child to completely dismiss reading and the importance of books. This rejection then becomes to some school officials "nonadaptive behavior."

> What about the stuff you read in school? It wasn't interesting to me . . . Dick and Jane went up the hill to fetch a pail of water and all that crap. Mary had a little lamb. Spot jumped over the fence. See Spot jump over the fence. I mean I got this stuff in the seventh grade too . . . Dick and Jane was in the house. Mom and Dad was going to the market. Spot was outside playing with the ball with Sally. I say ain't this the cutest little story. And I took the book one day and shove it straight back to the teacher and said I ain't going to read that stuff.[60]

A study of texts used in Trenton, New Jersey, and many other schools throughout the state, conducted by the Cadwalader Parent-Teacher's Association, indicates that the texts used in New Jersey schools are no better than those used elsewhere. The authors conclude:

> On the basis of these findings, it is clear that the material presently being used at all levels in the Cadwalader school are highly unsatisfactory in respect to both illustrative and subject matter.
>
> Only three of 46 volumes considered in the study on subject relevance were adjudged "highly relevant" to the

environment of the reader—the inner city child. It would seem imperative that the materials currently being taught at Cadwalader, and indeed all over the country, be looked at long and hard, regarding their suitability for this day and age. What percentage of our youngsters still live in a big, white house, with sweeping green lawns, and a picket fence? How many have gone horseback riding or visited the circus? It is high time publishers of educational materials re-evaluate their material and begin with all due haste to bring them up to date.[61]

More important than the content of the textbooks, the newness of the school building, or any other factor is the quality of the teacher. This has been understood for thousands of years; as Plato said, "I maintain that every one of us should seek out the best teacher he can find, first for ourselves, and then for the youth, regardless of expense or anything." [62]

A more contemporary educator has noted: "Perhaps the key figure in the entire educational process is the teacher. Good teachers can work miracles with children coming from any background; poor or uninterested teachers never seem to succeed, even with children of good backgrounds." [63]

Many certified teachers, however, will not go to the ghetto areas, such as the Central Ward in Newark. Despite the fact that poor children need competent teachers more than anyone else, a commitment to educate the poor is largely nonexistent. Carl Marburger, State Commissioner of Education in New Jersey, has recently commented, "People [teachers] are leaving the big cities because they have no commitment." [64] Neither comment is made in ignorance of the difficulties that teachers face. It is true, as Silberman has noted, that "Teachers refuse to teach in a white slum school because of the problem of discipline, because of fear of personal safety, because of experiences of having the tires on their cars slashed or the windows broken, etc. The fact that a school is in a Negro slum merely compounds the problem." [65] But the question remains to be answered: Do we not have the human and financial resources necessary to educate the poor children of America at a time when we are sending Peace Corps volunteers to underdeveloped nations on the other side of the world and are orbiting spacecraft around the moon?

As Haubrich has written, "Teachers do not view teaching in culturally depressed areas as a distinction, and the biting issue is that our society does not usually view it as a distinction." [66] He offers a typical situation:

> Eileen Morse received her appointment as a regular teacher from the Board of Education. One look at the address was enough—she and thirty-four out of one hundred appointees to this Borough decided they weren't having any. The influence of the press—"always looking for a good story"; of parents—"you'll type before you teach in that neighborhood"; of a fiancé—"you nuts or something"; of friends—"one could do it, I suppose"; all these and more had effectively done the job of turning Eileen to other schools in other places. . . . As one principal put it, "Who will we get to cover the classes?" Each year the same question; each year the same Eileens.[67]

The problem is exacerbated each year as the number of Eileens gets larger. Commissioner Marburger has recently indicated that there are 1,650 teaching vacancies in New Jersey and that this number has risen 10 percent in the past year.[68]

Then who does *cover* the classrooms? To insure that there are enough teachers so that at least there is an adult present to maintain order, the depressed-area schools have to hire ESRP's, Emergency Substitutes in a Regular Position. Sexton indicates that in Big City,

These ESRPs make up a large part of the teaching staff in some areas and, as might be expected, they are heavily concentrated in lower-income schools. . . . The students whose parents' incomes are below $7,000 per year have ESRPs 17.9 percent of the time. Students whose parents earn more than $7,000 annually have ESRPs 5.5 percent of the school day. . . . The heavy loading of ESRPs in lower-income groups indicates that children in these groups have what must be termed "inferior" teachers.[69]

On the basis of this research in New York and other cities, Clark indicates that "Schools in deprived communities have a disproportionately high number of substitute and unlicensed teachers." [70] For a number of reasons the problem of unqualified teachers in the urban areas of New Jersey may be particularly acute.

In some cities, as the proportion of Negroes in the population has risen, the quality of the teaching staffs has declined sharply. For example, in Washington, D.C., "In 1955, 16.4 percent of the teachers employed had temporary status—without tenure because of failure to meet the prescribed qualifications. In 1965, 40 percent of all teachers had temporary status." [71]

The difficulty in recruiting and keeping qualified teachers in depressed-area schools is not solely a function of the attitudes of the teachers. The indifference to the needs of the disadvantages is built into the personnel policies of the school system. "It is no secret that in many cities across the country, the depressed areas have been the 'Siberia' of the local school system, and those who for a variety of reasons were to be disciplined were sent to these undesired schools." [72]

The penalty meted out to the teacher often causes bitterness which is projected at the only vulnerable target available—children the teacher never wanted to teach in the first place. One teacher, commenting about life in depressed-area schools, noted, "There is a lot of brutality—brutal beatings, and nobody cares—nothing is done about it." [73]

The slum schools not only are repositories for castoff teachers, but the "promotion" system of the public education program guarantees that teachers will consider it rewarding to leave. As the Allen Report indicates:

> A spurious "reward structure" exists within the staffing pattern of the New York schools. Through it, less experienced and less competent teachers are assigned to the least "desirable" yet professionally most demanding depressed area schools. As the teacher gains experience and demonstrates competence, his mobility upward usually means mobility away from the pupils with the greatest need for skilled help. The classrooms that most urgently need the best teachers are thus often deprived of them. [74]

Studies by Howard Becker[75] and Robert Havighurst, both in Chicago, substantiate the contention that depressed-area schools have the least experienced teachers. Havighurst notes:

> . . . Younger teachers and those with least experience tend to be assigned to schools in the lower socio-economic areas . . . teachers over 50 years of age and with 16 or more years of experience are heavily clustered in the higher status and in the mixed, middle and working class areas . . . the median years of teaching experience of regularly assigned teachers in these [low income] schools is only four compared with 19 for teachers in the most favored. [76]

Sexton indicates that in Big City "inexperienced teachers (as well as unqualified teachers) tend to be concentrated in lower-income schools." [77] Commenting on this fact, which appears to be a nationwide phenomenon, she continues: "It seems likely that, other things being equal, an experienced teacher is much to be preferred to an inexperienced teacher. . . . a teacher can become expert at her job only through experience, and expertness is as necessary in teaching as in any other occupation. . . . low income and nonwhite pupils, especially in inner-city schools, receive an inferior quality of instruction." [78]

Analyzing the quality of teaching and its importance on a nationwide basis, the Coleman Report indicates: "The average Negro pupil attends a school where a greater percentage of the teachers appear to be somewhat less able. . . . the better the quality of the teachers, the higher the achievement; and . . . teacher differences show accumulative effects over the years in school." [79]

An additional problem of depressed-area schools is the high turnover of teachers. Clark has written that in some classrooms the teacher may change as many as ten times a year.[80] High teacher turnover exacerbates the problems of discipline and motivation for the child to learn. It is impossible for a teacher to develop teacher-student rapport in a short period of time, and each changing face indicates to the disadvantaged child that no one is really interested in his education. Thus the next teacher's task is that much more difficult. The failure of a new substitute to interest all the students in education is to a major degree a function of his fresh arrival and early departure: "Friday we had a substitute in class named Mr. Fox, and I had a headache so I went to sleep. (Why were you sleeping? Were you out late the night before?) No, I wasn't. I just had a headache . . . They wasn't doing nothing but talking. About this and that, Sally and John, and I just went to sleep. The class wasn't doing nothing but fussing, fooling around, talking so I went to sleep." [81]

Richard A. Cloward and James A. Jones have written that "because of the greater turnover of teachers in slum schools, their relative inexperience and the geographic mobility of low-income families, slum youth actually receive less instructional time than do children in middle-class neighborhoods." [82] Deutsch has noted that as much as 80 percent of class time in a depressed area is spent on a combination of disciplining children and on organizational details. This compares with 30 percent of time spent in middle-class schools. [83]

The disadvantaged child particularly requires a stable relationship with the same teacher to counter the instability of home life. One teacher emphasizes this point in a general analysis of the relationship between the middle-class teacher and the depressed-area school:

> Some classes are taught regularly by substitutes, thus duplicating rather than countering the instability of homes where aunts and grandmothers appear seriatim to take on the care of younger children; at the end of the day the teachers charge for the exits, some to moonlight jobs, others to the safety of a better neighborhood, and at the end of each term several always announce that they've had it, and off they go to the suburbs. To function at all, such a system requires subterfuge: the promotion of illiterate children, the pretense that the sick are well, that the rebellious are docile and that massive stagnation is progress. [84]

Effective teaching requires that the teacher gear her techniques and methods of instruction to the background and educational needs of the student. Obviously, disadvantaged children have to be taught differently from middle-class children. Frank Riessman notes what he believes to be the better teaching style for the disadvantaged educational situation: (1) Physical and visual rather than oral; (2) content-centered rather than form-centered; (3) externally oriented rather than introspective; (4) problem-centered rather than abstract-centered; (5) inductive rather than deductive; (6) spacial rather than temporal; (7) slow, careful, persevering (in areas of importance) rather than quick, facile, flexible. [85] But whether one agrees with Riessman or not, the main point is that there are differences in learning styles; as Arthur Pearl has written, "Schools must be prepared to meet and treat with the poor child on his own level as he enters." [86]

Teachers in the depressed areas lack the ability to alter their instruction to the needs of the impoverished child because they have not been trained properly. As confusing as it may appear, the orientation of teacher-training programs reflects the rigid educationist's view that all children are the same. "The professional sequence [of teacher-preparation courses] in most cases, views the content of teacher preparation as a universal, and applicable in all normal school situations. Teacher preparation in college classrooms and student teaching in school X has point and substance in schools Y, Z, etc. Student teaching is probably the culmination of the sequence, and a license is issued to a graduate. He is 'prepared.' Kids are kids." [87] This is reinforced by another authority: "A major reason for the inappropriateness of teaching methods in lower-income schools is that teacher training institutions persist in training all teachers as though they were going to be fed into the suburban middle-class school." [88]

A second deficiency that stems from the inadequate training of teachers is their ignorance of the cultural and ethnic backgrounds from which their students come. Very few middle-class members of our society know much about famous American Negroes or Puerto Ricans; however, for the teacher, ignorance of these matters is especially unfortunate. It is probably accurate to say that the vast majority of depressed-area teachers have never taken a single course on the Contribution of the American Negro in American History, for example. This course, or one like it, is probably not offered in the majority of teacher-education programs in the nation.

Thus we should not be surprised at the inability of our

teachers to gain rapport with minority-group disadvantaged students:

> Recently, a student teacher was attempting to show the pattern of immigration to the United States. She listed the Irish, the Germans, the Italians, the English, and the Scandinavians; she also indicated through class discussion the contributions these groups had made. Even though the class was entirely made up of Negro and Puerto Rican children, she made no mention of Negro or Puerto Rican immigration, inmigration, or contributions. When asked why this was so, she indicated that she did not know about these things, for they were not part of her college work or her own reading.[89]

In part because of mediocre education, and also because teachers are part of the American middle-class milieu, teachers in the depressed areas are discriminatory. This bias takes a number of different forms. There are many examples of teachers who are not free of overt ethnic bigotry. One study describes the attitudes of teachers in a Southwestern United States school where the student body was 57 percent Mexican-American:

> A teacher asked why she had called on Johnny to lead five Mexicans in orderly file out of a school room, explained . . . "His father owns one of the big farms in the area and . . . one day he will have to know how to handle the Mexicans." Another teacher following the general practice of calling on the Anglos to help Mexican pupils recite in class, said in praise of the system: "It draws them [the Americans] out and gives them a feeling of importance." [90]

The principal of this school expounded the tracking system initiated under his administration: "We thought that the white children would get more out of school if they could work faster and not be slowed down by the Mexicans. We thought the Mexican kids would do better work if they were in classrooms geared more to their level. . . . Everybody is happy about the grouping programs. . . . The Mexican parents have never said anything. . . . I guess the Mexicans are more comfortable in their own group." [91] A verbatim report from a conversation with a teacher in New York brings the presence of prejudice closer to home:

> As soon as I entered the classroom, Mrs. X told me in front of the class, that the parents of these children are not professionals and therefore they do not have much background or interest in going ahead to college. . . . She discussed each child openly in front of the entire class and myself. . . . She spoke about the children in a belittling manner . . . her over-all attitude was negative in that she did not think much of the abilities of her students. She told me in private that "heredity is what really counts," and since they didn't have a high culture in Africa and have not as yet built one in New York, they are intellectually inferior from birth. [92]

And the words of a child stirred by the teaching of Mrs. Lawana Trout, National Teacher of the Year in 1964, suggest a disturbing experience. "One boy responded immediately: 'I once had a teacher who was always screamin' and yellin' at us. You dirty little colored kids are ruining our schools,' he mimicked." [93]

In many instances discrimination by the teacher takes a socio-economic form; education then becomes a class struggle between teacher and student. As Pearl has written: "Unfortunately, we have a lot of teachers in predominantly disadvantaged schools who should not be there. A lot of them are prejudiced, not necessarily because of their children's racial or ethnic background but because the values and mores of these children are opposed to the values and mores of the middle class from which most of their teachers come." [94] And Clark adds: " 'The clash of the cultures in the classroom' is essentially a class war, a socio-economic and racial warfare being waged on the battleground of our schools, with middle-class and middle-class aspiring teach-

ers provided with a powerful arsenal of half-truths, prejudices, and rationalizations, arrayed against hopelessly out-
classed working-class youngsters." [95]

Perhaps one example of this type of prejudice is illustrated when the teacher stridently demands that the student
conform to her idea of proper hair style, or dress fashion,
both irrelevant to the process of education. Either the student capitulates or he suffers the teacher's recriminations.
"The teachers would start on the hair and go on down to the
dress. Cause I was getting this scene a lot of times. Telling
me to get a haircut . . . 'No I'm sorry. I don't need one.'
'Why don't you get a haircut?' '. . . I wear my hair the
way I want.' " [96]

Furthermore, a study by Helen H. Davidson and Gerhard Lang indicates that teacher reaction to tertiary considerations such as dress and hair style is so great that even
when the child is a good student, the teacher's attitudes are
not altered. Not even high grades change the teacher's
biased attitude. And the children, Davidson notes, perceive
this attitude.[97]

The most insidious form of discrimination, which infects
perhaps the majority of depressed-area teachers, is the belief, often unexpressed and sometimes unconscious, that
while the impoverished Negro or Mexican-American child
may be equal in potential to others, the damage done to him
at home cannot be overcome. There are numerous ways
that this discrimination is communicated to the child such as
through patronization or condescension, but the central
idea is that the child is incapable of learning. Thus the
teacher resigns himself to the child's failure. As a field representative for the National Education Association has
commented: "They [the disadvantaged children] are relegated to the arena of the untouchable, unteachable, unde-
sirable, where nothing is expected of them. People treat
them as if they are nothing, have nothing (including brains)

and will amount to nothing. Hence they end up with nothing
—having never really had a chance." [98] As Riessman has
noted, sometimes this behavior is well meant—though it is
no less harmful.

> Academic standards are lowered because it is felt the educa-
> tional tradition and aspirations of these children make it
> impossible for the teacher to demand more. The many peo-
> ple who defend these practices feel that they are being con-
> siderate and sensitive to the needs of children. Actually they
> are being too "understanding" in surrendering to the level
> at which the child seems to be. Perhaps, it is not the disad-
> vantaged who have capitulated to their environment, but the
> teachers who have capitulated to theirs.[99]

Educators and psychologists are aware of the impact of
the self-fulfilling prophecy. "The deficiencies of the slum
school are further aggravated by a widespread belief that
the intellectual capacity of most slum children is too limited
to allow much education. As a result standards are lowered
to meet the level the child is assumed to occupy. Frequently
the chance to stimulate latent curiosity and excitement
about learning is irretrievably lost, and the self-fulfilling
prophecy of apathy and failure comes true." [100]

When a young child is told either directly or through the
attitudes of the teacher that he is not intelligent, the child
will often accept the denigration and begin behaving as if he
were, in fact, stupid. Tests given to the Mexican-American
children in the study mentioned earlier verify this fact: "Sociometric tests . . . disclosed that even the Mexican children come to share the view constantly held up to them that
the Anglos are 'smarter' and their good opinions of special
value. Repeatedly told they are 'dumb,' the children begin
to behave in that pattern." [101]

The prophecy seems to be part of the atmosphere in
many classrooms where the Miss Abernathys teach: " 'Miss
Abernathy, there's not a child in this room who can read

fifteen words. Few of them work; they can't read.' 'They've been well taught, Miss Burke. All our teachers are doing their best.' " [102]

The most blatant example of the existence of the self-fulfilling prophecy at work exists in Camden, New Jersey. The Special Education system in this city utilizes information charts about the children which specify an IQ "saturation point." This point represents a level, estimated by a psychologist, beyond which the child is supposedly unable to progress. It is not surprising, then, that as one teacher in the program said, "You'd be surprised at how accurate the saturation point levels are, there are very few children that go above them." [103] This practice continues despite the fact that not a qualified educator in the country would deny that unsatisfactory environment can deter intellectual growth and cause a child to be placed in a Special Education class in the first place.

However, examples appear concerning the effect that teaching has when it is based on positive expectations. One teacher in discussing the qualities of a "good" school mentioned:

> It's eighty years old, with multiple wings and stairs like ours; there are hundreds of places for children to hide—and they never do. Every child is in his room all day. Low truancy, zero lateness. The school reads on grade level. The principal is a Negro woman but that's not the point. She has the same cross section of teachers as anywhere else. They come from the same school board, same distribution of assignment. But this level is what she demands . . .[104]

As Peter Schrag has commented: "After all the arguments about slums and deprivation, about buses and the 'neighborhood concept,' . . . if you insist that the kid learn something, he will learn; the most severe shortage in education is one of people who believe that idea and have the courage and skill to act on it." [105]

Until recently the proof that the teacher's low estimate of the disadvantaged child's ability could interfere with learning was largely garnered through personal observation and sociometric tests. Indirect evidence was also available from rat experiments which indicated that they performed better when their mentors were told they were bred for intelligence,[106] but this was inconclusive.

Robert Rosenthal, however, has dramatically documented the fact that children do well when the teacher believes the child to be bright. He told teachers in a San Francisco elementary school that certain students had been evaluated by IQ tests and were found to be on the verge of an academic "spurt ahead." In fact, the children were chosen in random-sample fashion. After one year of experiencing the self-fulfilling prophecy, the "spurters" showed higher IQ gains than the control group which represented the rest of the student body, an IQ gain of 12.22 points, compared with 8.42. Even more dramatic gains were registered later, however. The IQ of the "spurters" increased 27.4 points in the first grade and 16.6 points in the second grade, as contrasted with control-group advancement of twelve points and seven points respectively. Rosenthal also noted that Mexican boys whose faces were somewhat Anglo-Saxon, as opposed to identifiably Mexican, showed higher gains.[107] Clearly, if teachers treat children as if they are bright, they will act that way. Conversely, there is much evidence to suggest that if a teacher believes a child to be a dolt, the child will behave that way.

But the inequality of education goes beyond the inhospitality of the school to the poor, the inadequacies of teachers, and the irrelevance and biased nature of the curricula materials. Educational plants and educational facilities are also inferior. This inequality, which jolted James Conant's notion of the meaning of equality in 1961, has not been remedied. The Coleman Report of 1966 for the Northeast

Region of the United States, including New Jersey, at the elementary school level, indicates, for example, that the American Negro student is disadvantaged in terms of the age of the main school building, average pupils per classroom, number of schools with a gymnasium or cafeteria, the number of textbooks and a central school library.[108]

The pattern in inequality continues in high schools and includes, beyond almost all of the factors already mentioned, less access to physics, biology and language laboratories; absence of an infirmary and a full-time librarian; texts under four years old, and fewer average library books per pupil.[109]

Commenting on this aspect of their paper the authors note: "Just as minority groups tend to have less access to physical facilities that seem to be related to academic achievement, so too they have less access to curricular and extracurricular programs that would seem to have such a relationship." [110]

As Sexton indicates, however, the inequality of educational facilities is a socio-economic class problem; the crisis in education transcends racial demarcations, and this is true in urban and rural areas across the nation as well as in Big City. Sexton further indicates that despite the popular belief that "class size is smaller in lower income areas where students tend to be harder to handle and in need of extra attention by the teacher . . . , class size is not smaller in lower income areas; in fact it is somewhat higher." [111] This pattern of overcrowding and inferior school facilities has been found in Washington, D. C. "Despite the fact that 70 per cent of all elementary schools constructed since 1958 have been placed in areas where the median yearly income is below $6,000, the oldest, most overcrowded schools continue to be in the poorest parts of the city." [112] In 1965, 5,652 children in Washington, D. C., were attending class in rooms intended for other purposes.[113]

In his attempt to alert New Jersey citizens to the educational plight of the poor, Commissioner Marburger notes: "These [depressed-area] schools lack many essentials, including in many instances a modern physical plant and first-rate equipment." [114]

If our society really investigates the suffering of a life of poverty in America, perhaps we will find that the greatest inadequacy is the educational starvation which has confronted poor children over the years. As the late Senator Robert Kennedy stated, part of the problem is one of educational methods: "We pass bills and appropriate money and assuage our consciences, and local school systems keep right on doing things the way they've done them for decades. . . . The kids in the ghetto will never recover unless we do something right now." [115]

But as the Senator himself was aware, this is only a minor part of the problem. The schools are failing to educate the disadvantaged child because we, as a society, are failing to face up to the dilemmas of poverty. Because of ignorance, indifference and selfishness, we have not demanded free, equal public education. When all the liabilities of the present system are added up, it seems miraculous that the percentage of impoverished children designated as mentally retarded is so low.

≈ V.

The Health Crisis
of the Poor

Poverty is having a child with eye trouble and watching it grow worse every day, while the welfare officials send you to the private agencies, and the private agencies send you back to the welfare, and when you ask the welfare officials to refer you to this special hospital, they say they can't—and then when you say it is prejudice because you are a Negro they deny it flatly—and they shout at you: "Name one white child we have referred there." And when you name twenty-five, they sit down—and they shut up—and they finally refer you, but it is too late then because your child has permanently lost 80 per cent of his vision—and you are told that if only they had caught it a month earlier, when you first made inquiry about the film over his eyes, they could have preserved his vision.[1]

MORE THAN the loss of her child's vision—and the loss of his chance to enjoy a normal life—the words of this mother speak of a moral blindness on the part of society. It is a blindness which has made it possible for human lives to be written off with callous indifference, if not openly in the name of class or racial prejudice, then more subtly in the name of bureaucratic procedure. In the context of current discussions about welfare and anti-poverty programs, it must not be forgotten that the most massive attempt to do something *for* the poor will pale in comparison to what has already been done *to* the poor.

It has been written often enough in the earlier pages of this monograph that what society likes to call "mental retardation" among the poor—and, indeed, the poverty-inflicted organic damage that actually does impair the intellectual function—is related to a whole complex of conditions which the poor are forced to endure. None of these conditions is more important than the poor person's physical and mental well-being—his "health" or lack of it. No member of the middle class who knows that he himself would prefer to avoid the handicap of a variety of chronic conditions or that he would prefer to spare his child the brain damage that comes of poor prenatal care needs to question the relevance of this discussion.

One of the few persons to come to grips with this problem—and certainly one of a tiny minority within the medical profession—is Dr. H. Jack Geiger of the Tufts Comprehensive Community Health Action Program:

> The health of the poor in the United States—and the health services available to populations in poverty—represents a major, ongoing national disaster, a part of the special human disaster that is extreme poverty in an affluent society. We have known the general dimensions of this disaster for a long time, just as we have known about the relationships between poverty and health, without fully facing up to either of them. The poor are likelier to be sick. The sick are likelier to be poor. Without intervention, the poor get sicker and the sick get poorer. And that is just what has been happening,

and is happening today, in the central cities and ghettoes of the urban North, the sharecropper's shacks of the rural South, in Appalachia and elsewhere.[2]

Dr. Geiger's words should not come as a revelation. More than fifty years ago Edward T. Devine analyzed poverty and discussed its linkage with ill health and other factors.[3] Over thirty years ago the need for comprehensive medical care for the entire population—nonexistent then as now—was spelled out.[4] And several decades ago the U. S. Children's Bureau pointed out what is now well known—that infant mortality rates increase as family income decreases.[5]

Yet the Tufts program demonstrates that the problem is getting worse, not better. Dr. Geiger notes that the gap between rich and poor in the area of health care is widening,[6] and his colleague, Dr. Count D. Gibson, Jr., reports that the mere presence of the Tufts program has brought to the surface an array of health conditions that were barely known to exist in such quantity.[7] A number of recent studies, one in Hunterdon County, New Jersey, have shown that about 50 percent of the serious illnesses in the total population are untreated.[8] It should not be too difficult to determine who it is that suffers from these illnesses.

A major clue is provided by Dr. Alonzo S. Yerby, who states that in 1957 in New York City "43.8 percent of all adult recipients of public assistance were reported to have some kind of chronic illness or disability."[9] Additionally, "many others of low income who are not on assistance do not receive any care, and the very neediest do not necessarily receive their share of the benefits in public programs."[10] Three other facts are relevant: even where medical vendor payments are guaranteed to recipients, the quality of care and facilities is likely to be poor;[11] caseworkers concern themselves with the eligibility of recipients and with clerical details, rather than with medical problems;[12] and "medical care tends to be viewed as another commodity—an item in a public assistance budget. Welfare administrators and their medical advisers have shown little comprehension of the nature of medical care services or of the unique contribution that a good medical care program could make toward the reduction of dependency." [13]

The problem of welfare and the dependency it breeds will be discussed more fully in a later section of the paper. But because welfare should be a major source of health care for persons who might otherwise receive none, it is useful to consider the viewpoint of Mitchell Ginsberg, the former New York City Welfare Commissioner: "Social welfare programs are basically designed to save money rather than to save people. And the tragedy is that all too often they end by doing neither." [14]

Another part of the tragedy is that the people whose lives, or at least whose well-being, are squandered are children. Dr. Yerby reports that of 329,000 persons on welfare in New York City in 1960, 142,000 were under eighteen years of age. "These children depended entirely on publicly supported medical services for pediatric care, immunization, dental service, and care of all acute and chronic conditions. If private or public agencies did not provide this care, the children simply would go without." [15] And "going without" is precisely what happens in many cases. In the decade ending in 1963, medical vendor payments for welfare recipients increased nine times. Yet only 8 percent of this increase was accounted for by families in the Aid to Dependent Children program, who represent half of all public welfare recipients.[16]

The dilemma of the welfare recipient is shown by the fact that every cent of the allotment must be used for immediate needs. One welfare mother, with a monthly check of $406, "estimated that her monthly expenditures were: food, $150;

rent, $111; clothing, $20; gas and electricity, $15; cost for care of her son Christopher, three, while she works, $52; employment expenses, $20; household supplies, $7; laundry, $7; personal items, $12; school expenses, $5; and roach killer, $4. The total: $403." [17] In this accounting not enough money is left for a single visit to a doctor, or for scarcely any other health measure.

The result of this typical situation is that the poor suffer to a staggering degree from almost every physical and emotional malady known to man. Among these conditions are cardiovascular disorders, rheumatic fever, heart disease, diabetes, cancer, prematurity, infant mortality, schizophrenia,[18] dental disorders, arthritis,[19] rheumatism, visual impairments, general mental disorders[20] and many others. "There may be some rare conditions that the poor resist better than the rich," writes Dr. George James, "but we have not yet found it." [21] He substantiates this statement by a study conducted in New York City, in which the death rates of five of the ten leading causes of death for Flushing, a white middle-class area, were compared with those of the impoverished and heavily Negro Bedford-Stuyvesant district: "In each case in Bedford the death rates from these causes were higher than for the city as a whole, and lower in Flushing than for the city as a whole. The causes include the cardiovascular-renal group, cancer, diabetes, the pneumonia-influenza group, and accidents. . . . if the city as a whole could maintain its health record at the level of that of Flushing, as regards deaths from various causes, 13,000 lives a year would be saved in New York City." [22] Concludes Dr. James: "It is no exaggeration to state that these deaths are caused by poverty." [23] But if these deaths have poverty at their root, their immediate cause is a set of diseases and conditions which is not beyond the means of society to control or eliminate when the necessary priority is placed on doing so.

Numerous other statistics demonstrate the preponderance of health problems among the poor. Tuberculosis rates are one such source of information: in 1963, the rate of newly reported cases of TB in Flushing was 20 per 100,000. By contrast, the rate in the Lower East Side was 183 per 100,000, and in Central Harlem it was 226 per 100,000 —eleven times as high as that of Flushing.[24] In 1964, East and Central Harlem, with 24 percent of Manhattan's population, accounted for 40 percent of its TB deaths. Bedford-Stuyvesant, with 9 percent of Brooklyn's population, accounted for 24 percent of its TB deaths.[25]

Another indicator is the fact that the largest number of those who are rejected by the Armed Forces for physical reasons come from a poverty environment.[26] Moreover, while half of all such white rejectees were already receiving care for their condition, only 16 percent of the Negroes and 10 percent of the Puerto Ricans were receiving care.[27] Commenting on this fact, Dr. James notes: "We often chide ourselves for not having disease detection programs numerous enough and effective enough to find all the diabetes, glaucoma, and cervical cancer we could do something about. But these draftees are people whose conditions are *found;* and if we can not do something for conditions we know about, we are in bad shape." [28]

For some impoverished groups, conditions are so bad that the very life span of the population is reduced. Among Indians, for example, life expectancy of the infant is eight years less than for infants born in the United States generally. Many Indian infants don't even have to wait that long to find out how far they will fall short of the national average: the infant death rate among Indians is 60 percent higher than the national average.[29] But perhaps the best indicators of the health conditions among the poor are the statistics at the Institute of Industrial Relations at UCLA, concerning the Watts section of Los Angeles:

. . . the Watts area contained only 17 percent of the city's population, but in category after category it harbored nearly 50 percent of the city's ills. It had 48.5 percent of amoebic infections, 42 percent of food poisoning, 44.8 percent of whooping cough, 39 percent of epilepsy, 42.8 percent of rheumatic fever, 44.6 percent of dysentery, 46 percent of venereal disease, 36 percent of meningitis and 65 percent of reported tuberculin reactors. The death rate in Watts was 22.3 percent higher than for the remainder of the city.[30]

These statistics were gathered five years *before* the Watts riots. It is quite clear that the killing had begun long before the violence of August, 1965, and it is clear, too, that the killing was not done by the slum dweller.

One of the major deprivations in Watts—and one which goes far toward explaining these statistics—is its almost complete lack of medical facilities: "In the hard-core area of Watts, there is no hospital of any kind. Around the periphery are eight proprietary hospitals, only two of which are accredited. There is no emergency service available to the 344,000 residents of Watts except in unaccredited hospitals or in hospitals miles beyond its borders." [31] The contrast between the needs and the facilities of Watts stands at the heart of the health problems of the poor. It is just one more illustration of what Dr. Derek Robinson calls "the aphorism that the most needy communities tend to have the least adequate facilities for coping with their problems." [32] It should be added that this situation is hardly a coincidence; these communities are needy precisely *because* they lack facilities, and, at the same time, they lack facilities *because* they are needy.

The health status of the poor person, then, is similar to other aspects of the impoverished life: it is both a reflection and a cause of his low socio-economic status. Negroes, it should be mentioned, are trapped in this cycle to a greater degree than other groups,[33] but a number of studies have shown that "within specific economic groups in the two populations, differences [in disability and medical care] between the white and nonwhite populations tend to decrease." [34] The disproportionate amount of suffering by the Negro seems to be largely a reflection of his disproportionate representation in the lowest classes of society. It is worth noting, too, that low status, from a medical standpoint, should be determined on the basis of a number of indices, including low income, inadequate education, unemployment, overcrowding, parental composition, school-age illegitimacy and juvenile delinquency.[35] It is well to keep in mind, however, that the most useful of these indices in determining some aspects of health status, such as mortality rate, is low income.[36]

The impact of low income and the other indices of medical poverty on health care have been well catalogued. One of the most revealing pieces of information concerning the complexity of factors involved is a study of pregnant women in Boston. This study noted that the percentage of women receiving satisfactory prenatal care was directly related to income *and* to the educational level of the women. "Where education as well as income was low, the percent with adequate care was far less than for women with either income or education or both in their favor." [37] In view of the close relationship between poor prenatal care and mental retardation, the Boston study demonstrates the meaningful relationships which G. H. T. Kimble discusses: "It is bad enough that a man should be ignorant, for this cuts him off from the commerce of other men's minds. It is perhaps worse that a man should be poor, for this condemns him to a life of stint and scheming in which there is no time for dreams and no respite from weariness. But what surely is worse is that a man should be unwell, for this prevents his doing anything much about either his poverty or his ignorance." [38]

A number of studies substantiate, in more general terms, the medical deprivations that are associated with poverty. In 1954, Earl Lomon Koos demonstrated that the poor are given fewer health examinations, benefit from fewer immunizations, hold fewer health insurance policies, and engage in fewer public health activities than members of the middle and upper classes.[39] A decade later the United States Department of Health, Education and Welfare released statistics which leave little doubt that poverty appears closely associated with a wide range of indicators of medical deprivation. In the area of hospital and surgical insurance, for example, only about one-third as many poor people are covered as are rich people. While 34.1 percent of people in families with incomes of two thousand dollars or less have hospital insurance, 87.5 percent of people in families of incomes of seven thousand or more hold such insurance. The figures for surgical insurance are 28.8 percent and 83 percent.[40] It is worth noting, too, that the percentage of those who hold these insurance cushions is closely related to educational level as well as to income.[41]

Another indication of deprivation among the poor is that they utilize hospitals less frequently.[42] If the difference between the income groups in this category is not as drastic as in the area of insurance, it may be because, as HEW suggests, "among higher economic groups some hospitalization, or repeated or prolonged hospitalization, may be avoided by early diagnosis and preventive care." [43] But with regard to the percent of the hospital expense *covered* by insurance, the differences between the income groups stand out. While no part of the hospital bill was paid by insurance for 60.4 percent of the lowest income group, this was true of only 19 percent of the highest group. On the other hand, while three-quarters of the bill or more was paid for by insurance for 61.2 percent of the highest group, only 26.7 percent of the poor were assisted to this extent.[44] Reviewing these figures,

Anselm Strauss remarks: "Strangely enough, however, cash difference [money actually spent for care] is not nearly so great . . . Clearly, the poor not only get poorer health services but less for their money." [45]

The figures on money spent for health care to which Strauss refers show that the amount spent per person per year for health for the $2,000 and under group is $112; for the next two groups—$2,000 to $4,000 and $4,000 to $7,000—the figures are reasonably close: $116 and $119. Only when one reaches the $7,000 and above level does the figure jump to $152.[46] An earlier study by the U. S. Department of Labor, however, shows that for the very poor and the very rich, there is a tremendous gap in this area: "the 2.4 per cent of families with incomes under $1,000 spent only one-seventh as much as an equal number of families receiving $15,000 and over." [47]

But even with the HEW statistics, one can see an alarming difference between the lowest and highest groups with respect to health care for *children*. The amount spent annually on a child from a three-person family with an income of $7,000 or more is *five times* greater than the amount spent on a child in a seven-member family with an income of $2,000 or less.[48]

A further indication of this neglect of poor children is found in another set of statistics—those dealing with the number of physician visits per person per year. The HEW study showed that there are only 4.6 visits for persons from the lowest income group, as compared with 5.7 visits for persons from the highest group.[49] This difference, of course, is significant in itself. As HEW noted: "Since persons in the lower income groups have higher rates of disability due to illness and injury . . . than those with larger incomes, it appears that the lower rate of utilization of physician services results from lack of funds or for reasons other than need for such services among persons in low income families." [50] But it should be observed that the utilization of physician visits increases not only with increasing income but also with increasing age. The number of office visits per year for the poor child, fifteen years of age or under, was 1.6, as compared with 5.7 for the rich child.[51] Once again, the young among the poor are deprived more than anyone else, a fact which aids in explaining the higher rates of retardation and environmental deprivation among poor children.

An even better indication of the causes of poverty-linked retardation is seen in the statistics on use of specialists by the poor, particularly specialists involved in care related to the well-being of the mother and the child. While only 9.6 percent of children fifteen years old or younger in the lowest income group visited a pediatrician, 29.4 percent of the children in the highest income group made such visits.[52] Similarly, while 3.5 percent of the women in the lowest group visited an obstetrician or a gynecologist, 17.1 percent of the women in the highest group made use of these vital services.[53]

Other studies confirm these findings: A New York City study found that "a[n] . . . obstetrician attended almost 50 per cent of single live births of white mothers where the baby's father was a professional or executive, but only one-fifth this proportion where the father was a laborer." [54] And in Alameda County, California, it was found that 66 percent of the white women married to professionals had taken the Papanicolaou Test for cervical cancer, while only 47 percent of those married to laborers had done so.[55]

In less vital but still important areas, the same sort of discrepancies appear. The person in the highest income group, for example, made three times as many dental visits and three times as many dental X-ray visits and spent three times as much for dental care as the person in the lowest group.[56] More than *half* the persons in the lowest income group (51.6 percent) had never been to a dentist or had not visited a dentist for at least five years, as compared with 18.8 percent in these categories for people in the highest income group.[57]

One of the most revealing sets of findings is reported by Patricia Cayo Sexton, who describes an area in which the educational and the medical establishments have merged their failures—the area of health care for schoolchildren.

Mrs. Sexton reports, for example, that 20.9 percent of the children from families with incomes of three thousand dollars and under have not received smallpox vaccinations, as against 3.9 percent for children from families with incomes of nine thousand dollars and over. The respective figures for diphtheria-tetanus vaccination are 18.9 percent and 1.7 percent.[58] "The situation is even worse in the small, minor income groups. In one of these groups (the second-lowest income), 30.8 percent of all students did not receive smallpox vaccinations, and 27.5 percent did not receive diphtheria-tetanus shots." [59]

Even greater neglect is seen in the more general area of health examinations. In the low-income group, 49.3 percent did not receive routine health examinations, as compared to only 7.0 percent for the highest group.[60] "More evidence that low-income children do not get the kind of medical attention they need comes from the records of school nurses. According to nurses' reports, lower-income children are much less likely to receive medical attention recommended by school nurses than are upper-income children." [61]

Even where defects have been diagnosed, the poor children suffer from neglect. Among the lowest income group, 31.1 percent of the children who were found to have vision defects received no treatment for the condition. The figure for the highest income group was only 13.5 percent. For hearing defects, the figures were 53.2 percent for the lowest group, and 34.6 percent for the highest.[62]

It is not surprising, in view of this neglect, that poor

children of school age suffer from illness to a much greater extent than their richer peers. Out of every ten thousand children in the lowest income group, 7.9 contracted rheumatic fever; this contrasted with 2.6 among the highest group. For tuberculosis, the rates were 6.8 per ten thousand for the lowest groups and *zero* for the highest; for diphtheria, the rates were 15.1 and zero.[63]

There is one additional group of statistics which shows a significant correlation with income. The school attendance rate for the lowest income group was only 90.4 percent, as against 93.2 percent for the highest.[64] Similarly, there were 10.7 enrollment losses per ten thousand due to illness for the poor group, and only 5.3 per ten thousand for the highest income group.[65] The attendance and enrollment figures, moreover, do not reflect the situation of the child who is able to attend school, but whose neglected handicaps—such as the hearing and vision defects mentioned above—make it impossible for him to perform according to his potential.

It was noted earlier that a low level of education is often reflected in low levels of health and health care. Now the reverse relationship is discovered: poor health care may be reflected in poor attendance and performance in school. What generalization emerges from these statistics is that the vicious cycle of poverty is nowhere more vicious than it is in the area of health. Indeed, a proper understanding of the total problem requires that this area be given careful consideration.

It is not difficult to marshal documentation for Dr. Charles Mayo's summation of the interrelationship between poverty and illness: "sickness makes people poor . . . poverty makes people sick." [66] The Bureau of Labor Statistics, for example, reports that poor health is the second leading cause of subemployment.[67] Conversely, Dr. James reports that poverty is the third leading cause of death in New York City.[68] These findings tell the simple story: a man becomes sick; he loses a steady income; he becomes poorer; he becomes sicker, and he dies.

The case of those who do not die should be examined in greater detail. "Individual poverty," writes Charlotte Muller, "is primarily the result of factors which block gainful employment at an adequate wage." [69] One of the most significant factors in producing poverty—and, again, one of the most significant results of poverty—is chronic illness.

The relationship between chronic illness and economic status has been known for a long time. A study in 1931 showed a marked correlation between the two.[70] Several years later, the National Health Survey revealed that the rate of chronic illness for persons on relief was about two and one-half times greater than the rate for persons with incomes of one thousand dollars to fifteen hundred dollars.[71] The latter group, it should be noted, was by no means rich; it was only not as poor as the former group. One is left to wonder how great the gap would be between the poor and the really well-to-do.

More recently, the Department of Health, Education and Welfare has found that the percent of the population with one or more chronic conditions was 57.6 for the group with a family income of two thousand dollars or less, and only 42.9 for the seven thousand dollars and above group.[72] But if the HEW study substantiates the earlier findings of a positive relationship between poverty and chronic illness, it also demonstrates the reverse relationship. For while the higher-income groups do suffer from chronic illness, their activity is not generally limited as a result of it. For the poor, on the other hand, chronic illness limits activity more than *three times* as much as for the highest income group.[73] For the most serious chronic conditions, the gap is even greater. Activity is limited by heart conditions four and a half times as much for the poor as for the highest income group; by high blood pressure almost six times as much; by mental and nervous conditions more than six times as much; by arthritis and rheumatism almost seven times as much; and by visual impairments more than eight times as much.[74] The poor, in addition, suffer five times as much mobility limitation from chronic illness as do the rich, and almost five times as many are confined to their homes.[75]

The result of this situation, not surprisingly, is that persons from the lowest income group have more than *twice* as many disability days per year as do persons from the highest income group.[76] As HEW notes in another study, "it is evident from these published data that a sizeable proportion of the middle-aged 'poor' population suffer serious physical limitations in their ability to work." [77]

An even more convincing demonstration of the interrelationship between chronic illness and poverty was reported by P. S. Lawrence in 1948. Lawrence observed the changes in status and illness for white families in Hagerstown, Maryland, over a period of twenty years. On the one hand, he found that "The percentages of persons ill or dead from chronic disease in 1943, according to change in socio-economic status from 1923 to 1943 are: among individuals with reduced status, 40.9; same status, 25.1; improved status, 13.9. This relationship is statistically significant." [78] On the other hand, he discovered that "chronic disease is a more significant factor in causing reduced socio-economic status. Of the families in which there was no chronic illness in 1923 or in 1943, none had a reduction in status and 21.6 percent showed an improvement. Of those families which had no chronic illness in 1923, but which in 1943 reported illness or death from chronic disease, 9.2 percent suffered a gross reduction in status while 9.5 percent 'improved.' " [79]

The demonstration that the relationship works both ways only begins to tell the story. As Lawrence notes, one must take into account the fact that chronic illness, when it strikes, affects not only the ill person but his whole family. Thus, while 18.8 percent of the individuals studied were suffering from chronic illness in 1923, 55 percent of the family members examined were affected.[80]

There is, moreover, a tendency for several illnesses to occur simultaneously. Dr. Robert Straus, noting what he calls the "clustering principle," reports that nine out of ten of Kentucky's rural poor exhibit multiple pathology.[81] Dr. Charles H. Goodrich reports the same thing for the New York Hospital-Cornell Medical Center, where the recipients of welfare medical care are found to require many hospital services.[82] And in Newark, Dr. Shirley A. Mayer outlines the high-risk conditions among five new patients at a Project Clinic and points out that "Although the five examples above are outlined as though there were only one high-risk condition per patient, in reality, they are doubly and triply compounded. The medical conditions are superimposed upon the social high-risk factors. They are multi-problem families." [83] Other studies have shown that poor children coming for care for the first time presented a long backlog of untreated illness,[84] and that for poor people, the complex of degenerative diseases start to "take their toll" after the age of forty-five.[85] The process at work in these instances has aptly been labeled by Dr. James as "the avalanche phenomenon." [86]

In one sense, the avalanche phenomenon has the meaning given to it by Lisle C. Carter, who writes of the poor: "When they are uneducated, they are unskilled; when they are unskilled, they may well be unemployed; when they are unemployed, they are trapped in the low-level social environment which created the health hazards and the poor opportunity." [87] In another direction, the avalanche phenomenon has the effect observed by Charlotte Muller: "Medical expenses of the aged parent turn the income of the adult children away from educational uses. Prevention of disabling conditions in childhood is an investment in adult earning capacity. One may ask, in addition, what happens to motivations and expectations concerning achievement when there is one persistent major health problem, or a series of problems which cumulate to overwhelm the low-income family." [88] One could extend the list of the ways in which persistent health problems jeopardize the chances of the poor almost indefinitely. The critical mother-child relationship discussed earlier in this paper, for instance, is severely damaged by serious illness to either mother or child. The very task of assessing one's problems, in fact, is made difficult or impossible in the face of a painful, annoying physical condition.

But the ultimate result of the avalanche phenomenon is best characterized as an emotional rather than a physical ailment. The anxieties, the frustrations, the lack of fulfillment of the poor person make him far more susceptible to mental illness than is the person from a higher-income group. Studies by Krugman,[89] Hollingshead and Redlich,[90] and Cornell University (the "Midtown Study")[91] have all demonstrated this fact. Commenting on the Midtown findings, Michael Harrington points out that "the stress factors listed by the Cornell study are the very staff of the life of the poor: physical illness, broken homes, worries about work and money, and all the rest." [92] For Harrington, the culture of poverty itself is best described in terms of the psychological disorientation of the poor:

> Indeed, if there is any point in American Society where one can see poverty as a culture, as a way of life, it is here [among the poor who are mentally ill]. There is, in a sense, a personality of poverty, a type of human being produced by the grinding, wearing life of the slums. The other Americans feel differently than the rest of the nation. They tend to be hopeless and passive, yet prone to bursts of violence; they are lonely and isolated, often rigid and hostile. To be poor is

not simply to be deprived of the material things of this world. It is to enter a fatal, futile universe, an America within America with a twisted spirit.[93]

But where Harrington provides an insight into the problems of the poor by showing that their "culture" can be considered an emotional disorder induced by the circumstances under which they live—and where this paper has attempted to show a close relationship between the culture of poverty and mental retardation—others have pushed the concept of the "twisted spirit" even farther. For them, the concept has been employed as the central element in an explanation of the health problems of the poor.

A great deal has been written concerning the "life style" of low-income groups, particularly regarding their attitudes toward health care. Koos, in one of the classic statements on the subject, has described the feelings of anonymity, resignation and present-orientation of the poor.[94] Health care, for this group, assumes a rather low place in the hierarchy of values.[95] The poor, in fact, have an entirely different conception from the middle class as to what illness is and as to the worth of treatment.[96] The approach of the lower class to health care, as interpreted by Koos, is summarized by this reaction of a lower-class housewife: "There's a lot of things I know you're supposed to do something about, but there's a lot of reasons why you don't. . . . I'd look silly, wouldn't I, going to see a doctor for a backache. My mother always had a backache, as long as I can remember, and didn't do anything about it. It didn't kill her, either. . . . If I went to the doctor for that, my friends would hoot me out of town. That's just something you have, I guess. Why let it get you down?" [97]

The same ideas have been reiterated by Lola Irelan, for whom the health behavior of the poor is characterized in terms of their "fatalism," their "preference for particularistic and personalized relationships," and their "more concrete, materialistic modes of thinking and talking." [98] Noting that concepts of health differ greatly in different societies, Irelan speaks of a culture in which a person is considered to be sick only when he is unable to carry on his daily activities, and in which there is otherwise little interest in public health and preventive programs.[99] Leaning heavily on Koos, Irelan repeats his quote of a lower-class housewife: "If something was wrong with my husband, we'd get it fixed right away. He earns the money and we can't have him stop work. I can drag around with my housework, but he can't drag around and still earn a living." [100] Other studies reveal the same attitudes. Both Goodrich and James, for example, have found that very few among the poor made use of the Cornell Medical Center when it became available for welfare recipients.[101] Jerry Solon noted that patients tend to structure their medical care according to their "socioeconomic characteristics." [102] And Charlotte Muller points out that the poor are far more likely to ignore symptoms of disease, to treat these symptoms with inferior substitutes, or seek help from someone other than a doctor.[103]

It is undeniably of great importance to recognize that the health *needs* of the poor are different from those of other groups in society. As Anselm Strauss remarks, medical organization is not designed at present to deal with the problems of the poor; rather, it is geared to the patient who is educated and well motivated.[104] "I contend," he writes, "that the poor will never have anything approaching equal care until our present medical organization undergoes profound reform. Nothing in current legislation or planning will accomplish this." [105] The same laudable sentiment is found in Dr. Wilbur Hoff's admonition of public health workers to make their program relevant to the *values* of poor people.[106]

But at this point a serious difficulty is encountered. The

more one speaks of the unique values of the poor, rather than of their unique needs, and the more one characterizes their life style as an unfortunate creation of the poor themselves, which makes it impossible to provide them with health care, then the more one wanders from the source of the medical deprivations of the poor. "There is a possibility," writes Raymond Class, "that their behavior stems from poverty rather than their poverty from their behavior." [107] It will be the purpose of the remainder of this section to explore precisely that possibility and to determine where the responsibility lies for the deplorable health conditions among the poor.

In the first place, even the middle class exhibits a certain degree of bewilderment in the area of health care; the poor are not alone in this respect. As Koos demonstrates, the middle class often reacts with fear and confusion to health crises. Its sense of what constitutes illness, like that of the poor, often depends on a variety of circumstances.[108]

But more importantly, a great deal of evidence shows that, as Dr. James G. Haughton has written, "utilization [of medical facilities by the poor] is not a problem when services are made responsive to the needs of the population served." [109] The United States Conference of Mayors has echoed this by noting that "public and private services were being effectively used by the recipients, but . . . these resources were so inadequate that needs simply could not be met." [110]

Other evidence comes from Philadelphia, where "every new prenatal care facility for the indigent . . . has been used fully from the start";[111] from Boston, where more than one hundred persons visit the Tufts-sponsored health center each day and where more than 80 percent of the residents of Columbia Point have made visits within the first ten months;[112] from the Bronx, where a program of sending doctors into the homes of poor persons has met with an enthusiastic response;[113] from the Lower East Side, where a group of low-income persons have taken the initiative in planning their own community health program;[114] and from Howard University, where it was reported that lower-income individuals were successful in preparing their own health-education material.[115]

A great deal of justification exists, therefore, for the contention that the "hard-to-reach" might better be referred to as the "unreached." [116] These "unreached" demonstrate a great deal of strength in their efforts to maintain the well-being of their families: "When the great handicaps these mothers were enduring in day-by-day living are considered, the tremendous job they were doing becomes evident. Most of them had to be both mothers and fathers to their children. Though they lacked the emotional support, co-operation and companionship of a husband, they were managing on less than the minimum income considered necessary for health and decency. Their housing conditions were deplorable and their neighborhoods vicious and degrading." [117]

The economic obstacles to adequate health care, it should be reiterated, are overwhelming; no amount of analysis of the culture of poverty should be allowed to obscure this fact. Inadequate resources was the prime reason for poor prenatal care in Philadelphia. Moreover, "many hospitals demand all or a large part of the total fee for maternity care before they will accept a patient for prenatal care." [118] It has also been pointed out that convalescence is so expensive that "to put it bluntly, *the poor person actually cannot afford to recover from illness*. And without the chance to get better, he only increases his chances of getting sick again." [119] As Dr. Yerby has written, outpatient departments are accompanied by all the stigma associated with charity, yet they are no longer free.[120] Even when the health service is free, the cost of traveling to a clinic may be so great that the poor person cannot afford it.[121]

With this situation in mind, the poor mother should not be regarded as indifferent to her child if she buys two loaves of bread instead of paying several bus fares to take the child to a well-baby clinic. The priorities of the poor are exactly like the rest of society: the poor, like the middle class, are concerned primarily about survival. The observation that the poor lack a future orientation misses the point. The conditions under which the poor person lives *force* him to concentrate on his immediate needs; he prepares for the future by insuring that he will be alive in the morning.

Beyond inadequate income as a source of poverty-bred poor health, there is the very environment of poverty. If, as Rene Dubos has written, health is a "never-ending . . . adaption to the total environment," [122] it should be apparent that the roots of the health problems of the poor are more closely related to their shabby surroundings than to their own "health practices." A suitable adaption to these surroundings simply may be impossible.

Poor people lose out wherever they live: "They are very likely to live in the rural South or in a big city ghetto—neither of which is an area where good health care resources commonly exist . . ." [123] Both areas have their own special disadvantages. "There are a number of health hazards," writes Robert Straus, "which are magnified in a rural environment. These include snake, insect, and animal bites; dangerous thorns and poisonous plants; fungous infections; the danger of accidents inherent in farming, lumbering, mining and other predominantly rural occupations; the infectious diseases which man can acquire from animals, and the restricted opportunities for isolated rural people to develop immunities to some of the common infectious diseases of man." [124] And as Straus immediately adds, "All these problems are magnified by the conditions of poverty; contaminated water; inadequate sewage disposal; crowded living space unprotected from heat, cold, insects, vermin or rodents; inadequate clothing, especially shoes; nutritional deficiencies; meager education, and physical and cultural isolation from the concepts and resources of modern hygiene and health care." [125]

A third lengthy elaboration of unlivable rural conditions must be included with the other two; it describes the accommodations provided for migrant workers on many of New Jersey's farms:

> At one farm in Vineland, Negroes have been crowded into chicken coops. In another, they cook, drink and bathe from a foul water tap that has been grossly polluted by a nearby privy that has overflown. In every camp flies swarm over the garbage-strewn dust, the young children and the cooking grits and stolen vegetables that migrants usually live on.
>
> At night in the camps as many as six or more children are stacked like cordwood onto one roach-infested bed. . . . Many children have distended navels, indicating malnutrition, and many also are ridden with lice and ticks. Worm-infested infants, left unattended in the camps for hours by their mothers in the fields, are sometimes bitten by rats.[126]

But New Jersey with its severe rural poverty is also the most urbanized state in the nation;[127] it is in the city, moreover, where the health of the poor is most seriously jeopardized. As John W. Gardner, former Secretary of Health, Education and Welfare, has said, "The fate of the urban poor and the urban Negro is bound up with the fate of the city and the city is in grave trouble." [128] One need go only as far as the slum basement to discover just how grave the situation is. "Probably the most dramatic example of health problems relating to poverty," writes Dr. Howard Rusk, "is rats." There are as many rats in New York City as there are people,[129] a fact which is an excellent reflection of the general conditions of slum life: poor housing, poor sanitation and poor enforcement of health codes.

To a degree, the health problems of the urban poor are characteristic of urban populations in general. Lewis Herber has summarized the problem this way:

> Throughout the day the city dweller breathes the most noxious fumes of motor-vehicle exhausts, the solids, vapors, and gases emitted by domestic and industrial furnaces. His drinking water may be perfectly clear to the eye and laboratory tests may show that it is free of harmful bacteria, but there is a good chance that it contains traces of pesticides and industrial wastes, especially if the water is acquired from rivers in densely populated areas. . . . Although these day-to-day insults to the human body and nervous systems do not necessarily result in a sudden, acute illness, taken together there seems to be little doubt that they are very harmful. In fact a large mass of statistical information of respiratory disorders, cancer, heart disease, and mental illness establishes all too convincingly that we are steadily approaching a crisis in the field of urban public health.[130]

The urban poor face more intense dangers than those of other city dwellers. Herber reports the results of an experiment in which a colony of Norway rats were forced to live in conditions of extreme congestion—similar to conditions for humans in Harlem and the Central Ward of Newark. Displaying a wide variety of deviant behavior, "in sixteen months the rats had regressed to a state where their extinction was assured." [131]

Dr. Ellis D. Sox has pointed out that "the major part of a man's life is spent in a dwelling unit," and that largely for this reason, the areas of San Francisco in which the most substandard housing is found are also the areas in which physical and social pathologies are most prevalent.[132] He suggests that "The slums of our cities were not created by the occupants, but by the failure of code enforcement agencies to provide strict and consistent enforcement." [133] The same point was made repeatedly at a conference on Negro health at Howard University; substandard housing, for which the poor pay exorbitant rents, and which is allowed to persist through lack of code enforcement, is one of the chief problems affecting the health of the poor.[134] Lack of enforcement affects the condition of the hospital itself, as well as that of the dwelling: "At Fordham Hospital alone, 100 violations were reported. They ranged from debris, insects and rodents in various rooms to unsanitary handling of medical equipment and excessive dust on the ceiling above infants' cribs." [135]

It was noted earlier that recovery from illness is often beyond the financial means of the poor; it should be pointed out here that the poor lack a suitable environment at home for convalescence to take place,[136] but the environment of poverty may endanger health in more active ways than that. On the one hand, it subjects its inhabitants to such hazards as burns resulting from poor heating equipment;[137] on the other, it helps to produce various types of mental illness and social disorders.[138] "Monotony, isolation, and barrenness": those are the words used by Dr. Gibson to describe the environment of the Columbia Point ghetto.[139] Dr. Donald K. Freedman has labeled the American ghetto a "traumatizing environment."

The relationship between urban poverty and health has been discussed at greater length by Dr. Leonard J. Duhl, who has written of a "pathological urbanization," characterized by complexity, loss of identity and poverty.[141] What is needed, under these circumstances, is a more comprehensive approach to the problem of health: "Health cannot be regarded separately from other problems in society. We cannot divorce our concern for mental and physical health from the problems of crime and delinquency, of unemployment and poverty, of inadequate housing and education. Health is a total community phenomenon. It is related to everything that affects the human being." [142] Others have recognized the same need. James A. Kent has proposed that health care become a "permeable area" through which the poor may be able to participate more broadly in the larger society.[143] And M. I. Roemer has maintained that medical care is better defined in social science terminology than that of natural sciences.[144]

The medical profession's response has been almost exactly the opposite. Dr. Conrad Seipp reported that only one hospital in seven offers social services.[145] But this observation only begins to indicate the ways in which the medical profession has failed to deal with the problems associated with poverty. Fundamentally it has not provided basic health services to the nation's poor.

In rural areas, "we hear from counties that have no doctors, from communities without public health services of any kind, from places where children go to school without ever having come in contact with a health professional." [146] Of the cities, Dr. Yerby notes that they "have shown a unique and enduring propensity to create health problems" and then to do nothing about them.[147] To this, James adds the irony that "the city is filled with conveniences," and yet is unable to meet the health needs of its residents.[148]

As of 1965, comprehensive medical programs for the indigent existed in less than one-quarter of the states.[149] In some areas, the Negro poor cannot obtain *any* medical care.[150] Mental health services have been especially unavailable for most poor people.[151]

In one area this inadequacy is of particular significance. It is often said of the poor that they have no interest in preventive medicine; the real responsibility for this, however, lies elsewhere: "Preventive health services for preschool children in the Aid to Dependent Children program were found to be practically non-existent in Chicago in 1960 due to a number of circumstances. Only four clinics provided such services for children 2 to 6 years old; family budgets did not provide for the services of a private physician; and the Department of Welfare was not permitted by law to pay for preventive services." [152] In addition, as Dr. Milton Terris has pointed out, medical schools have traditionally ignored the areas of preventive supervision and public health.[153] In fact, writes Dr. Kenneth W. Clement, almost no preventive medicine is available for the poor.[154]

In New Jersey, the lack of medical care for the poor parallels the problem elsewhere. A survey of ambulatory services in the state's eighty-five general community hospitals "indicates that these services are grossly inadequate in terms of availability of services when needed, continuity of care, physician's time and that of other medical personnel and other auxiliary services including adequate records, social work and follow-up. Where services are available barriers exist inhibiting their acceptability to persons who need them." [155] It was also found that "few physicians are willing to practice in the affected neighborhoods." [156] Some indication of New Jersey's place in the national picture is given by the fact that the state stands *last* in federal grants-in-aid for health, education and welfare, a fact which, writes HEW, reflects the state's own unwillingness to spend large sums for public assistance.[157]

Dr. I. S. Falk has written that the weakness of modern medicine is the "gap" between its potential and actual service rendered.[158] The size of this gap in the United States is indicated by the thirteen thousand deaths due to poverty in New York City alone, by the neglect of those rejected by the draft for physical reasons, by the refusal to treat schoolchildren with curable defects. Public interest was centered recently on the case of a thirteen-year-old boy—the stepson of the owner of the Cleveland Browns football team—who was rushed to New York by helicopter to receive treatment for gangrene.[159] It is to engage in utopian fantasies to speculate on whether a poor child, living in the very shadow of the hospital, would have received the same kind of attention.

Even when the poor are able to obtain care, however, it is clearly second-rate. "The quality of care of the disadvantaged in many large public hospitals," writes Yerby, "has reached critical levels." [160] As one article on public health facilities asserts: "Since many cities can no longer afford to purchase care from the large, well-equipped voluntary hospitals in their midst, care of the indigent becomes concentrated in large, overcrowded, understaffed municipal hospitals where rapid bed turnover is a necessity because of the pressure of incoming patients. In some city hospitals, maternity patients with no obvious medical complications are released 24 hours after delivery." [161] A survey of thirty-three cities in 1961 showed that local health agencies in twenty-seven of them spent less than sixty cents per capita on health services for mothers and children, and twelve spent less than thirty cents. [162]

Dr. E. Richard Weinerman has revealed that outpatient clinics constitute the major medical resource of the poor. Only one-third of the group he studied reported having a regular physician, and that percentage was composed chiefly of individuals from the middle and upper classes. [163] Solon has demonstrated a clear correlation between income level and use of a hospital's outpatient department rather than of more comprehensive facilities. [164] The health care provided for the poor by the medical profession is "almost wholly episodic in nature," [165] which helps explain the high chronic-illness incidence among the poor. The more persistent conditions simply are not treated.

In the area of mental health, too, the treatment of the poor is inferior. The situation has been described this way: ". . . often legal means . . . force lower class schizophrenics into hospitals. Once there, they are likely to be treated organically or to be retained in custody without treatment. Even where financial capacity is ostensibly not a factor (as in public outpatient clinics) the lower classes are less often accepted for psychotherapy. In such public facilities, it has been found that less skilled staff members (e.g., medical students) are more likely to be assigned poorer patients. Lower class patients are treated for shorter periods and by less intensive techniques." [166]

Even more important than the inferiority of health care for the poor is what Dr. Geiger has called the "nearly insuperable barriers to access."

> . . . these include the barriers of time and distance—the remoteness of many health facilities, the long hours of travel and waiting time. The barrier of fragmentation—well-child care in one place, sick-child care in another, adult care in yet another, ambulatory care somewhere else, in-hospital care at yet another focus, social work and other specialized resources in still other locations. (Indeed, it might be said that—until the advent of new OEO health programs in the past year—there was only one health career job available to the poor. It was called "trying to get some help" and it was a full-time, often thankless, task.) The barrier of practical convenience, with hours and organization of health activities that make it almost impossible, for example, for the working mother with many children to hold a job, maintain the home *and* utilize preventive or therapeutic help. The barriers of cost and of confusing, complex, and contradictory eligibility requirements. The barriers of discontinuity, irrelevance and impersonality. . . .[167]

In 1962, there were fourteen different kinds of health services in California for children under eighteen years of age.[168] In Philadelphia, Dr. Lewis D. Polk has stated that while cost is no barrier to the public hospital, the discomfort of the long bus ride to the hospital is enough to prevent pregnant women from using it.[169] In Newark, registration and clinic procedures kept one-third of the pregnant women away.[170]

Attempts by the poor to obtain medical care invariably result in a runaround. Anselm Strauss relates the case of a worker who was unable to get assistance for his wife's post-operational complication until she was discovered "by accident" by a nursing student.[171] Fred J. Cook tells of a Watts infant with bronchitis, eczema, cow's milk allergy, umbilical hernia, right anal hernia, heart murmur, tonsillitis and an ear infection. The child's mother was put off so consistently by health officials that eventually she simply gave up.[172] The same pattern of official evasion is characteristic of attempts to get help for mental illness.[173] The entire situation is summed up by the woman, eight and one-half months pregnant, who was turned away from a prenatal clinic in New York after three hours of waiting because the hospital did not serve the area in which she lived.[174]

What is involved in these cases has been variously labeled "administered poverty" [175] and "bureaucratic sclerosis." [176] "It is a shame," chides James, "that people, especially deprived people, will not arrange themselves to fit neatly into fiscal and administrative categories." [177] To a large extent, the administrative dismemberment of the poor person is due to the growing specialization of the medical profession. It is due, too, to the tendency of all public assistance agencies to give up on those cases in which results seem impossible and to concentrate on those that seem hopeful. "Most of the 'do-good' agencies," writes Dr. Leonard Duhl, "would rather choose cases in which there was hope, and which did not offer the tremendous difficulties, the foreign ways, the resistance to changing to 'middle-class' ways of living, and which do not present problems of eligibility or complexity." [178]

More is involved in this situation than rigid adherence

to bureaucratic standards. Ample evidence suggests that lurking behind this adherence is a strong class bias. The poor have described it best; the mother of a polio victim put it this way: "Well, they don't tell you anything hardly. They don't seem to want to. I mean you start asking questions and they say, 'Well, I only have about three minutes to talk to you.' And then the things that you ask, they don't seem to want to answer you. So I don't ask them anything anymore." [179] Koos quotes a lower-class respondent as saying of hospitals that "You don't have anything to say about them, anyway—they're run by the big shots." [180] And the Northeast Neighborhood Association in Manhattan has said of Bellevue Hospital simply that "the impersonal handling of patients and general disregard for the dignity of the individual are strongly resented by community people." [181]

Evidence of medical disregard for lower-class needs comes from a variety of sources. It has been reported that Mayor John Lindsay, in touring New York City's hospitals in 1965, found at Harlem Hospital a mother holding a sick child. "The child was fever ridden and foaming at the lips, and the mother was moaning over it. Twenty minutes passed before a nurse even looked at the child . . ." [182] In the area of mental health, Anselm Strauss has had this to say: "There is a distinct danger, for instance, in the community psychiatry movement, that the professionals will assume they know a great deal about the communities and family settings of lower income patients—when really they do not. Most serious of all, perhaps, is the assumption again that professionals know what is good for these patients— after all, we are the experts and they are the non-knowledgeable, and sometimes uneducated, ill." [183]

Dr. Joel J. Alpert has found that assistance in maternal nursing care is directed at middle-class rather than lower-class families. [184] Solon has found that outpatient clinics are not sensitive to the needs of the poor. [185] An anti-poverty official has stated that health officials have shown little interest in possible health programs that could be supported by the Office of Economic Opportunity.[186] One study showed that "physicians whose patients were mostly Negro were less likely to initiate a discussion on family planning than those physicians catering only to white middle-class patients."[187] Dr. M. Y. Heshmat demonstrated that little effort is made to guide interested and able Negroes into the health professions.[188] It has been customary, in fact, for hospital staffs to refer to lower-income patients as "garbage." The attitude of the medical profession toward indigent patients is captured best by an anecdote: "There is a story about a medical school dean who said his students should have an opportunity to practice medicine on both paying and welfare patients. The paying patient would provide an opportunity to deal with people who make demands. The welfare patients would provide an opportunity for the students to see patients in an advanced stage of illness."[189]

Dorothy D. Watts has explored the factors associated with acceptance of modern medicine, and has found that these factors are closely related to middle-class characteristics.[190] Or, as Anselm Strauss has put it: "Those who understand, follow, respond to and are grateful for treatment are good patients; and that describes the middle class."[191] The reason why this is so has less to do with the patient, however, than with the doctor: "Professional health workers are themselves middle class, and represent and defend its values, and show its biases."[192]

The unique culture of the poor is in this area largely a reflection of the rigidity of the medical profession. The poor, like the rest of society, prefer to receive medical assistance from individuals whom they can trust and who seem concerned about their problems. Those who are not poor can turn to doctors for this kind of personalized attention; the poor, however, for whom the doors of the medical establishment have too often been closed, must look elsewhere for help: " 'People think of us as hard-core poverty cases. Well, you can look through every window two ways, and we look out and see what we call hard-core social workers, hard-core doctors, hard-core professionals of every kind.' "[193] It should not be regarded as even slightly remarkable that the poor frequently turn to chiropractors for help. Their reason for doing so makes a great deal of sense: " 'I've tried them all—every one of the doctors in town, an osteopath in B——, one of those physio-some-things in G——, and then the chiropractor down in the village. There's something he's got—I don't know what—that sure makes what he does for me right. . . . They can say all they want to, the chiropractor's got something when it comes to getting at what's wrong with you.' "[194]

The attitude of the medical profession toward the poor, however, sometimes goes beyond mere disdain, discourtesy and disinterest. On one hand, the poor are often subjected to open abuse. The atmosphere of a Midwestern clinic was described this way: "People are shouted at, ridiculed, abused, pushed around, called 'Niggers,' told to stand 'with the rest of the herd,' and in many instances made to feel terribly inferior if not inadequate."[195] A quieter kind of pain exists, too, such as that experienced by the Negro boy in Mississippi who said that he did not like to go to the doctor's office because he did not like going in the back door.[196] On the other hand, there are instances of unethical practices. It has been found that the poor may be subjected to such dubious practices as a routine urinalysis, a complete blood count, and one injection on every patient each month, munificent prescribing and continuing symptomatic treatment without established diagnosis.[197] Welfare recipients may be given as many as fifteen different drug prescriptions during a one-month period.[198]

The advent of Medicare and Medicaid, the programs of medical assistance for the aged and for the indigent, has not brought about the end of either type of indignity. One doctor referred to the Medicare patients with an "A Option" (those with coverage for hospital costs but not for the doctor) as "those cruddy A's." [199] As for unethical practices, the record is replete with them:

> A physician who billed Medicaid for an average of 65 house calls daily has been examining every member of the families of patients he visits whether he was sick or not.
>
> A number of physicians have overcharged for penicillin shots.
>
> Several dentists have billed for administering gas without indicating why the gas was necessary.[200]

The first of these abuses is particularly disturbing. Some doctors, it seems, are willing to provide comprehensive and preventive care only when it is financially lucrative. Yet the same old pattern prevails. Dr. Haughton notes that one agency arranged for physical examinations on children, "but failed to follow up when ailments were discovered." [201]

Several ironies involve the Medicare-Medicaid program. It was opposed by the medical profession partly because it would undercut the doctor-patient relationship. Yet the absence of that relationship was already one of the chief obstacles to health care for the poor. Secondly, Medicare has been unable to help some of the patients who need it the most, the impoverished Southern Negroes; this is because some Southern hospitals have made themselves ineligible by refusing to desegregate.[202] But the chief irony is that the new programs have been of greater financial benefit to the medical profession and supporting industries than to the poor. Doctors have been able to receive payment for patients whom they would have had to treat for reduced fees or for nothing in the past: "A nationwide survey by UPI reporters showed that this is one aspect of the new program that is very popular with the medical profession." [203] Dr. Milton Cherkasky, director of New York's Montefiore Hospital, believes that the proposal for doctors to bill the government directly is "motivated purely by a desire to charge more—it's as simple as that." [204]

Also profiting from the new programs have been the drug and hospital supply industries. One supply company, noting a Medicare-induced sales increase of 21 percent, stated optimistically that "operating is a sector of the economy that is virtually recession proof"; another pointed out that "this market—nursing homes and extended-care facilities of hospitals—is a great sales potential." [205] The nation's health insurance companies have also discovered "a greater opportunity for profits through Medicare." [206] New Jersey Blue Cross "is enjoying its best financial health in at least six years [due] . . . to the beneficial effect of Medicare," [207] yet its rates are spiraling, and it has been unwilling to provide outpatient care.[208] New Jersey Blue Shield rates have leaped to levels far beyond those of New York and Philadelphia, but "subscribers in the lower income levels will have to pay the higher rates without any saving in out-of-pocket expenses." [209]

The Bureau of Labor Statistics Consumer Price Index shows that increases in medical-care expenses lead all other categories.[210] Hospital costs in particular have been soaring.[211] For the poor, however, Medicare, and especially Medicaid, have not lived up to their original promise. In New York State, which has one of the best Medicaid programs in the nation, red tape has prevented more than three-fourths of the eligible persons from receiving benefits.[212] It has been alleged, too, that the medical profession in New York is trying to "price Medicaid out of existence" by charging exorbitant rates.[213] Congress has been aiding this tactic; the House of Representatives recently tightened the eligibility requirements in such a way as to remove the program from 10 percent of formerly eligible New Yorkers.[214]

New Jersey, of course, has no Medicaid program at all.

The great debate about Medicare-Medicaid is by no means over. For decades, the American Medical Association used words, money, political blackmail and cries of "socialized medicine" to fight it.[215] Opposition to the idea of health care as a right rather than a privilege is still the dominant position of the American Medical Association. But one basic contradiction in its position is as relevant now as it was before the passage of the new programs: "You can't have it both ways. American medicine has been proclaiming for years that no one who needs hospital care is failing to get it under the present system. Now, faced with Medicare, it cries that it will be swamped with new cases. It can hardly work both ways." [216]

Health care in the United States is not impressive in comparison with that of other countries. The United Nations World Health Organization found that in 1960 the United States ranked fifteenth in life expectancy for males and seventh for females.[217] Falk has pointed out that the United States compares poorly with other nations in the development of public systems of medical care.[218]

The responsibility for this failing lies more with American society generally than with the medical profession. The situation is typified by the recent action of the State of California, which has attempted to bring under control a "wild spending program" by cutting back the medical-care program for poor people. This cutback will deprive one and a half million poor persons of such "routine" surgery as hernia operations; of hospital stays longer than eight days; of all but the most essential drugs; of all dental care other than emergencies; and of all physical therapy, hearing aids and eyeglasses.[219]

Yerby has sought the roots of this attitude: "Medical historians have traced society's attitudes toward the sick from the primitive concept of possession by evil spirits, through the early Semitic notion of atonement for sin, and the Greek idea of constitutional inferiority, to the Christian belief in brotherly responsibility in which relief of the suffering promoted the salvation of the helper." [220] But the idea of Christian charity has not dominated the approach of American society to health care for the poor. From the earliest days, writes Yerby, care for the poor was provided by "Poor Law" medicine and by the almshouse. Need alone has never been enough to qualify individuals for public aid; the "Poor Law tradition of aiding selected groupings of unfortunates" has permeated even the most enlightened social legislation from the New Deal to the Great Society. "The Poor Law tradition," says Yerby, "lives on." [221]

This American system of priorities is not what one would expect from a world leader: "Sizeable welfare programs exist in the United States," it has been pointed out, "but they are less comprehensive and use a smaller proportion of the Gross National Product than those in any other advanced country." [222]

Senator J. William Fulbright has elaborated on this situation in specific terms: "Here are a few statistics on America's values: since 1946 we have spent 57.29 per cent of our budget for military power, 6.08 per cent for education, health and other social functions." [223] With justification, Senator Fulbright concludes—and thus provides the central insight into the health crisis of America's poor—that "the Great Society is a Sick Society." [224]

VI.

Welfare: The Cycle of Dependency

ANY ATTEMPT to understand the conditions which can impede the mental development of the poor must consider one of the most pervasive and destructive elements in their lives—that which they call "the welfare." In New Jersey, where more than 187,000 persons receive some form of public aid and where welfare rolls continue to rise, the problem is particularly acute. For beyond the fact that the state has been able to give financial assistance to a large number of people in need lies a growing recognition that what the state does not give and the way it uses what it does give are of great significance in making the lives of the poor intolerable.

The general failings of public assistance are too familiar to require extensive discussion. The late Senator Robert F. Kennedy, for example, struck a responsive chord in an audience when he described the situation this way: "We have created a welfare system which aids only a fourth of those who are poor, which forces men to leave their families so that public assistance can be obtained, which has created a dependence on their fellow citizens that is degrading and distasteful to giver and receiver alike." [1]

The degree to which this dependence is distasteful to the receiver has been well illustrated by recent demonstrations on the part of the welfare recipients in our nation's cities. The demands of these groups have been many; they have called for higher grant levels based on a national minimum standard, for the participation of recipients on local welfare boards, for improvements in food-distribution programs, for an end to "spying" by social workers, and for the establishment of procedures that would eliminate arbitrary, almost whimsical, treatment of applications by welfare departments. But the essence of their feelings was captured in a sign carried by a New York demonstrator: "We Want to Be Treated Like Human Beings."

The distaste for the present welfare system on the part of the giver, outside as well as inside the government, is also apparent. The attitude of many intellectuals is typified by that of Charles E. Silberman, who has indicted a welfare state which gives its greatest benefits to groups other than the poor. For Silberman, the three primary aspects of welfarism in this country are its middle-class bias, its inability to present the poor with a coherent program of funds and services, and its refusal to allow the poor to assume a meaningful role in the operation of the system.[2]

These criticisms have not been lost on the government itself, at least on the higher levels. The New Jersey Division of Public Welfare, in a 1966 Statement of Objectives, called for "a more integrated, more comprehensive, more simplified, more constructive, and more acceptable structure of public social services for New Jersey citizens." [3] The federal government has gone deeper; the Advisory Council on

Public Welfare—reporting to the Secretary of Health, Education and Welfare in 1966—advocated a system of nationwide public assistance standards for individuals whose eligibility is determined solely on the basis of need.[4]

Unfortunately, many welfare administrators, particularly on the local level, are less willing to recognize its degrading aspects. For these people, the most vital reforms are those which will assure that there is no cheating on the system. The well-publicized attempt to weed out potential cheaters in Newburgh (N. Y.) has had brutal sequels in Mississippi—where the traditional niggardliness of welfare administrators and other public officials has led to conditions of outright starvation—[5] and in Baltimore, where a number of welfare recipients, often illiterate and ill-informed, have been fined and given jail terms because of alleged frauds. In New Jersey, a Monmouth County Freeholder demanded that welfare records be used to prosecute the fathers of illegitimate children, and the Burlington County Welfare Board voted to cut off Aid to Dependent Children if it could be shown that there was a "man-in-the-house."

These instances of "welfare backlash" reflect a large segment of public opinion; they illustrate precisely why the dependency involved in welfare is so destructive of human dignity. American attitudes on the subject of welfare are, in a word, ambiguous: "While admitting that Society is, in some sense, 'responsible' for the culture of poverty so that social aid is necessary and proper, most Americans vaguely suspect that poverty could be relieved if the poor only tried to do something about it." [6] In view of the spirit in which aid is given, it is not difficult to understand the pain with which it is received.

Perhaps the most important relationship between welfare and mental retardation is the similarity in the popular approach to both problems. There is a tendency to keep the poor shut away in ghettos, just as the retarded are often shut away in institutions; to absolve society of guilt by blaming poverty on laziness, just as retardation is blamed on heredity; and to avoid, in both areas, the steps which would lead to prevention and rehabilitation.

If the subject of retardation can be discussed largely in terms of rigid institutions, the same is even more true of welfare. The public assistance system in the United States can best be described in terms of two self-perpetuating structures. First, there is the social service bureaucracy, preoccupied with its own procedures, concerned with its own survival, and operating with machinery that it designed to move slowly, if at all.[7] Second, there exists the subculture of poverty, increasingly dependent on welfare and forced, by necessity, to adapt its style of life to the demands of the welfare system. Completely beyond the specifically harmful aspects of welfare, therefore, is its greatest single failing: it helps to produce an unhealthy overall environment for poor people.

The way in which welfare contributes to the initiation and perpetuation of mental retardation among the poor is most clearly described in practical terms—that is, dollars and cents. The financial assistance provided by welfare is so inadequate that, while it may succeed in sustaining life, it achieves almost nothing in the way of ameliorating the hardships of poverty. As the Advisory Council succinctly stated, "Public assistance payments are so low and so uneven that the Government is, by its own standards and definitions, a major source of the poverty on which it has declared unconditional war." [8] The implication of this statement is that the whole range of factors which characterize poverty and which may lead to retardation—factors such as inadequate nutrition, poor prenatal care, psychological and cultural deprivation, and unsanitary living conditions—are left intact by our public assistance program. Small wonder that in Newark's welfare caseload, which consists largely of people in the second, third, or fourth generation of those on relief, three out of ten are suffering from serious congenital defects.[9] The same situation was revealed in a California study: "A senate committee in 1961 disclosed an alarmingly high incidence of physical and social pathology in families receiving Aid to Needy Children funds. Among ANC families in a study in Santa Clara County, it was reported, 13 percent had problems of mental deficiency, as compared with the estimated average of 3 percent for the general population." [10] Beneath such statistics lie deplorable instances of human misery, as is shown in this Monmouth County case study: "Mrs. S., mother of five children, was deserted by her husband after his final unemployment insurance check had been spent. For seven weeks Mrs. S. and the five children lived on a $30 a week food order from the municipal welfare officer. This occurred during the winter while three of the children had infectious hepatitis." [11] The obvious difficulty of welfare recipients in receiving adequate medical care is only part of the problem. While recipients may, with considerable delay and inconvenience, acquire help for specific diseases, mental retardation is not itself regarded as a disease. The health and nutritional causes are allowed to persist, due to the lack of appreciation of their long-range effect on human development.

The failure of welfare to deal with these long-range problems is best illustrated by reference to the financial situation of the people on relief. A family of nine in New Jersey, consisting of a mother and eight children ages 13, 11, 9, 7, 5, 3, 2, and 6 months—a not uncommon welfare family —received the rather meager monthly allotment of $359.60, according to state guidelines.[12] This figure does not include a number of special allowances which may be granted to the family under certain circumstances, but those may act to the detriment of the family. For rather than being able to live with the assurance that all the difficulties normal to any large family can be comfortably met, the welfare mother must rely on the dubious generosity of the welfare board in order to deal with each additional circumstance.

The basic monthly allotment is also exclusive of rent; the position of welfare boards is that they set no rigid guidelines on the monthly cost of rent. The practical effect of this position, however, is that the welfare board makes no effort to see that the recipient is provided with anything better than substandard housing. Indeed, the board may require that a welfare family move to "comparable housing" in which the rent is lower. The agony of dislocation seems to have less importance than the expenditure of fewer dollars.

One need not rely on cases as drastic as that of the Monmouth County mother in order to demonstrate the inability of welfare to allow recipients to lead normal lives. Even under the best of circumstances, welfare provides only the barest minimum in the areas of food, clothing, shelter and other necessities. A handbook prepared by the New Jersey Community Action Training Institute tells recipients that their food allowance is based on a very low-cost diet plan, and it warns them, as it must, that "buying a birthday cake may mean [that a woman on relief] has to do without something she really needs." [13] Certainly the inability of a welfare child to eat birthday cake with the happy abandon of a middle-class child bears no direct relationship to mental retardation. But it would be as absurd today to claim that the poor may enjoy the style of life led by the middle class as it once was to respond to the needs of the poor by crying "let them eat cake."

The disadvantages of life on welfare, whether hepatitis or the absence of birthday cakes, have the most severe psychological effects on poor children. The inability of public assistance to combat the physical and psychological deprivation associated with poverty, along with welfare's disruptive effect on family life, serve as a guarantee that the formative years of the poor child will not be suitable for normal development. The cycle of poverty—and retardation—starts with the child, and the influence of welfare on the child is such that it helps to perpetuate and intensify this cycle rather than to terminate it.

An improvement in the financial assistance provided by welfare—as one means of combating the poverty cycle—is not beyond the means of society. It was estimated in 1962 that the cost of raising every individual in the nation above the subsistence level would be about ten billion dollars a year—one-fifth of the cost of national defense.[14] Although public assistance expenditures in the nation have been rising, the proportion of personal income spent on public assistance declined from 1 percent to 0.7 percent from 1950 to 1965. Once again, the characteristic public approach to welfare—the refusal to place a high priority on the needs of the poor—lies at the heart of the welfare problem.

The public approach is based on the myth that the largest numbers of those on relief are the shiftless and the lazy, a myth which was rudely shaken by a recent federal study which showed that less than 1 percent of recipients are capable of being employed.[15] The same point had been made earlier in New Jersey in response to public dismay about increases in welfare costs, despite the expenditure of seventy-seven million dollars in the state in anti-poverty programs. The New Jersey Office of Economic Opportunity, in addition to noting that few on the relief rolls are employable, correctly argued that relatively small amounts of anti-poverty funds were aimed directly at manpower training rather than longer-range programs and that, in fact, the *rate* of increase in welfare costs had slowed since the beginning of the War on Poverty.[16] The view that public assistance in New Jersey is wasteful and unnecessary is also belied by the

Division of Public Welfare, which reported that in the fiscal year 1965, its "program operations continued to be crisis-orientated." [17]

In addition, if there is some lack of motivation on the part of recipients, a large part of the blame belongs to the welfare program itself. The long pattern of dependency, in combination with the unavailability of steady employment, is not likely to spur incentive or any other ingredient of success in middle-class society. One New Jersey analysis demonstrated that motivation to work, as one would expect, is partly a function of expectancy to work.[18] For many on relief, unskilled and broken by dependency, that expectancy has been entirely lacking for years. At the same time, reports the Newark study, "the popular feeling is that the individual on relief should gratefully accept any job." [19]

While the public continues to express its indignation over the expense of welfare, a disturbing truth is that relatively few of the nation's poor are being assisted at all. Senator Kennedy's estimate seems conservative; it is more likely that only a fifth of the poor are actually receiving help.[20] If this smaller group suffers from the popular misconception that all of its needs are being handled, so, too, the remaining four-fifths suffer from the unchecked fury of all the disadvantages of life in poverty.

What groups comprise this four-fifths? Many are simply individuals whose incomes exceed a state's eligibility standard but which fall below the federal poverty level—another indication of the need for a national standard. But many others fall victim to the stringent residency requirements of the states. Despite the increasingly mobile nature of American society, despite the fact that the poor are often forced constantly to move in search of work, and despite their frequent forced relocation, many fail to qualify for assistance merely because they do not meet the residency requirements of a particular state or area. A strange paradox is that such requirements may stand in the way of eligibility when the lack of American citizenship generally does not.

This problem is especially troublesome in New Jersey, where twenty thousand of the most needy persons—the migrant workers—cannot possibly meet the one-year residency requirements for most assistance. Recognition of this may be the first step (though there are many others) in understanding the staggering degree of apparent "retardation" among this group. Residency regulations also present difficulties for people newly arrived in urban areas and even for people who change their residence within the state.

The problem lies deeper than that, however; many persons who do not qualify for Categorical Assistance—Assistance for the Blind, Disability Assistance, Assistance for Dependent Children, Old Age Assistance and Medical Assistance for the Aged—are eligible for General Assistance. But this program, though intended to meet emergency needs and to fill gaps left in the Categorical Assistance program, is administered by municipal welfare boards which are usually even less eager to help the poor than are those on the county level. Moreover, of 567 municipalities in New Jersey, only 386 accept state funds and are required to report their programs to the state. In the rest, General Assistance, especially for transients, is often minimal or nonexistent.

Even more significant than residency requirements and the local autonomy of General Assistance is the division of the bulk of public assistance into rigid categories. Because of this division, welfare fails to reach most needy unemployed adults under sixty-five and most incapacitated adults who are not considered permanently and totally disabled. An additional effect of the rigidity of categories leads to absurdities. In Newark, "When individuals are rejected by the county as candidates for Disability Assistance, Aid to the Blind, etc., the city has no recourse but to classify them as 'suited for light employment.' Alcoholics, extremely obese persons, retarded people, and, occasionally, narcotics addicts are also classified, by default, as employable." [21]

The categorical approach, along with the system of matching federal and state funds, also means that "welfare programs are defined and developed to fit the available funds rather than the need for assistance or measures adequate to meet the need." [22] This means that states are more reluctant to participate in Aid to Dependent Children programs than in programs for the aged, blind and disabled, for which the federal government provides a greater proportion of the cost. The use of matching formulas also presents difficulties in nonfederally-funded welfare, in which the cost is shared by state and local governments. Accordingly, the New Jersey Division of Public Welfare has emphasized the need for (1) "a single formula of State-County sharing of the costs of all categorical assistance," and (2) a greater assumption of welfare costs by the state in order to relieve the disproportionate burden on local governments. Additionally, in order to avoid the long waiting period for Categorical Assistance—a period during which other help is often difficult to obtain—the Division urges that payments begin immediately on the basis of the principle of "presumptive eligibility." [23]

In New Jersey and in thirty-two other welfare jurisdictions, an even more serious problem remains—one that most severely affects children. For these areas have refused to take part in the program of Aid to Dependent Children with Unemployed Parents, a program intended to allow unemployed fathers to remain with their families without risking loss of welfare. The effect of this refusal has been disastrous for the poor family, and the policy has been decried by the New Jersey Welfare Committee in these terms: "Our public welfare program in New Jersey today operates in such a way as to perpetuate the matriarchal structure of the Negro family which existed throughout the period of slavery in America. It is structured so that the thousands of children growing in ADC families are damaged by the absence of their fathers from the home, and by the knowledge that this absence is the basic premise of their eligibility for a minimum amount of economic security." [24]

The denial of ADC-UP funds to New Jersey's children does more than deprive them of an opportunity to escape the physical hardships of poverty; in a real sense it seriously jeopardizes their chance to develop normally.

The financial inadequacy of welfare, however, is only a part of its detrimental effect. Equally important are the circumstances under which it is dispensed. The welfare recipient, it must be understood, lives an extremely insecure existence. In the light of potential disintegration of family life as discussed by Moynihan, it would be a mistake to minimize the fact that recipients are entirely at the mercy of welfare boards. Living on the whims of a group of individuals who often are not committed to the idea of welfare itself—and who must justify their decision-making by thinking up reasons *not* to grant assistance—is not likely to help to stabilize the lives of the poor. The welfare mother who is able to obtain employment and to arrange for some sort of daycare for her children does so at the risk of losing her welfare grant and even of being accused of fraud. The fact that she is often driven by necessity to augment her slim dole in this way has little effect in softening a welfare view which is geared to saying "no."

Moreover, the recipients' primary contact with the system is through the visitations of caseworkers whose function is often more investigative than sympathetic, and who are often poorly trained for their positions.[25] Welfare agencies make almost no effort to discover additional needy members of the community; they are quite active in declaring ineligible, however, those who believe themselves to be in need. A Monmouth County survey reported that only 9.5

percent of the recipients felt that caseworkers did anything more than determine eligibility.[26]

The Monmouth study also emphasized an equally important failure of the welfare program. "There is little or no attempt," it revealed, "to ascertain the causes of dependency, to ascertain the strengths of the recipients which could be built upon and bring about personal or economic independence, or to help the recipient plan toward a better way of life." [27] The fact is that welfare has a record of general failure in breaking the cycle of dependency because it concerns itself with peripheral services and not with the concept of rehabilitation and prevention.

The implications of this failure to mental retardation are vast. On the national level, the Advisory Council on Public Welfare has noted that "the lack of adequate social services for families, children, young people and individuals isolated by age or disability is itself a major factor in the perpetuation of . . . the widely deplored climate of unrest, alienation, and discouragement among many groups in the nation." [28]

This viewpoint was echoed more specifically in Monmouth County, where the study revealed an extensive need for services to dependent children and their families. Four crucial services mentioned were prenatal, confinement and postnatal medical care for mother and child; guidance and counseling for dependent children; improvement of home conditions; and, significantly, special programs for "individual children damaged by neglect or rejection." [29] That these services have been lacking in the past goes far to explain the perpetuation of the poverty-welfare-retardation cycle.

It is not surprising then that in Newark, where this cycle has been so persistent, "the City DPW (Department of Public Welfare) has been unable to provide its clients with the type of intensive long-range rehabilitative services that are prerequisite to achieving a goal of independent community living." [30] The anti-poverty program and related programs have made a start in the direction of providing needed services and opportunities, in areas ranging from day care to manpower training. But essentially the problem is related to a popular attitude which places a low priority on eliminating degradation and dependency in the welfare system. Until society is able to disabuse itself of the myths of welfare —as well as those of poverty and retardation—the old cycle is likely to continue.

The destructive results of the attitude of society is no better illustrated than in the area of child and youth welfare services. New York City authorities learned that the children who need help the most—"the losers"—are the ones most often rejected by the city's agencies. These are children who wind up at the Children's Center, a badly equipped, greatly overcrowded building where many youngsters remain indefinitely. It is not surprising that "their sense of rejection is overwhelming." [31] Nor would it be surprising if the great majority of these children are characterized, now and later, as mentally retarded.

The situation in New Jersey is scarcely better. The Passaic County Children Shelter in Wayne Township is a clean, modern building with pleasant surroundings. It would seem, at least superficially, to be a showpiece of enlightened treatment of deprived children. But it is severely overcrowded; it houses children ranging from murderers to those who are the victims of badly broken homes. All who can fit live in tiny cells; the others live together on temporary cots in a large room. No education is provided for the children; the only recreation area is a patch of blacktop completely enclosed by screening. No child is allowed out of doors. Those in charge seem more concerned about a single child escaping from the Shelter than about the probability that not a single child will escape from the maze of his own fears and frustrations. One child leaving the Shelter with his parents was told that if he were sent back he would never be allowed to leave again, "no matter how much you cry and scream." Another, requesting permission to read during a period set aside for resting, was thrown into his cell, the heavy door slammed behind him.[32]

"Social welfare," wrote a historian of the subject, "is special services supplied and material assistance given by all or part of society to a human being thought to be in need." [33] The ideal is a simple, yet noble one; but somewhere along the way it has soured. The helping hand characteristic of an earlier day has, for too many in society, become the slammed door. The effects of this kind of treatment on the human mind as well as on the human spirit have only recently begun to be fully comprehended.

VII.

Food Assistance
Programs

HUNGER AND MALNUTRITION stalk this land. Their existence has been overwhelmingly documented by the House Education and Labor Committee,[1] the Senate Sub-Committee on Employment, Manpower and Poverty,[2] the Senate Select Committee on Nutrition and Human Needs,[3] and the Office of Economic Opportunity.[4] The number of nutritionists, pediatricians, government officials, and the poor themselves who have appeared before these committees is huge; their message is the same: poor people throughout America are malnourished, desperately so. Conservatively, ten million Americans are affected; expert after expert has confirmed this fact.[5]

The original research which unearthed the national tragedy of widespread malnutrition in America was initiated by a group of doctors under a Field Foundation grant in Mississippi in May, 1967. The public report of the doctors' findings, *Hungry Children,* is devastating:

In Delta counties . . . we saw children whose nutritional and medical condition we can only describe as shocking— even to a group of physicians whose work involves daily confrontation with disease and suffering. In child after child we saw: evidence of vitamin and mineral deficiencies; serious untreated skin infestation and ulcerations; eye and ear diseases, also unattended bone diseases secondary to poor food intake; the prevalence of bacterial and parasitic disease, as well as severe anemia . . . in boys and girls of every county we visited, obvious evidence of severe malnutrition, with injury to the body's tissues—its muscles, bones and skin as well as an associated psychological state of fatigue, listlessness and exhaustion . . . We saw children who don't get to drink milk, don't get to eat fruit, green vegetables, or meat. They live on starches—grits, bread, Kool Aid . . . In sum, we saw children who are hungry and who are sick—children for whom hunger is a daily fact of life and sickness in many forms, an inevitability. We do not want to quibble over words, but "malnutrition" is not quite what we found . . . They are suffering from hunger and disease and directly or indirectly they are dying from them—which is exactly what "starvation" means.[6]

In 1968, two other reports which corroborated and expanded upon the *Hungry Children* statement were released to the public. *Hunger, U.S.A.,* a comprehensive report by a group of leading citizens, including lawyers, doctors, labor leaders, businessmen and nutritionists, indicated in hard, passionate terms that there is hunger and resulting malnutrition throughout America, and that there is very little being done about it.[7] The 1968 CBS television documentary, "Hunger in America," was a powerful, graphic portrayal of the hunger crisis of the poor.

If all the information above, which is based on field hearings and the knowledge of countless experts, is not enough to prove conclusively the prevalence of hunger among the poor, the January 23, 1969, statement of the preliminary findings of a national nutrition survey conducted by the Department of Health, Education and Welfare is. Nearly 17 percent of the twelve thousand people examined in Texas, Louisiana, Kentucky and New York were so malnourished that they required immediate aid. Thirty-four percent of the pre-school children examined were so anemic that they needed medical attention. Vitamin A deficiencies, so acute that blindness might ensue, afflicted 33 percent of the children under six. Kwashiorkor and marasmus, which indicate extreme malnutrition, and cases of rickets and goiter were discovered.[8] Dr. Arnold Schaefer, director of the survey, stated that the nutritional level of the people examined was as low as the level of nutrition found in similar surveys in Central America.[9] While the classical examples of malnutrition which are referred to above may exist largely in the South and Southwest, it is clear that serious malnutrition exists in every county in the nation.

The best way to understand this phenomenon, however. is to listen to a mother tell of the plight of her small children.

No fresh milk?
No sir
No milk for the children?
No sir
Do they get milk? The small ones?
No
No milk at all?
No
Ain't no one of them has milk every day. They lucky to have it twice a month.
And there are days without meat, or vegetables or fruit.
And days with only one meal or two—or three and they aren't really meals.
And the children go to bed hungry.[10]

It has been shown earlier in this study that poor nutrition—a condition directly related to poverty—is among the most significant causes of the organic damage that may lead to mental retardation. Some experts believe that malnutrition in a pregnant woman can cause permanent physiological damage to the brain of the fetus.[11] There is strong evidence that malnutrition plays a role in prematurity and that there is a high correlation between prematurity and birth defects including mental retardation.[12] There is also impressive evidence that severe malnutrition of an infant can cause irremediable brain damage.[13]

There are other dimensions of the impact of malnutrition on intellectual development. Poor children are more susceptible to diseases and infections such as pneumonia, colds and skin diseases because their natural resistance is lowered by inadequate nutrition.[14] The length of recuperation is also measurably increased because of the compromise that has been made with their nutritional intake. Children who are getting sick, are sick, or are recovering from sickness are not able to benefit fully from the stimulation that may exist in their home and local environment or from public education.

Malnutrition has very serious psychological repercussions. From birth the child is dependent upon his parents, and especially his mother, to take care of his needs and to provide a secure environment for him. Children who are hungry become insecure, suspicious and anxious. They become fearful of an environment that is noxious to them. If the hunger is chronic, the psychological impact can remain with the child forever.[15] Additionally, the human body appears to sharply moderate activity to suit nutritional status. Thus, when the body does not have enough calories and minerals to function normally, the behavioral pattern of the child is altered to suit the amount of energy available. The child is listless, dull and immobile because he hasn't enough energy to act otherwise. The lethargy of the hungry child can become a permanent behavioral trait as well.[16] Although the effects of malnutrition on the physiological, bio-medical and psychological well-being of a child are discussed separately here, it must be remembered that a ghetto child usually suffers some, if not all, of the ill effects of malnutrition simultaneously and synergistically.

How can children be hungry in this country? Many people assume that the federal food assistance programs insure that everyone has an adequate minimum diet. Unfortunately, this is not the case at all. The Department of Agriculture, the agency that administers the food assistance programs, has never been primarily interested in feeding the hungry. The department has seen its first responsibility as stabilizing and enhancing the income of farmers, and in this regard they have been mightily successful. The total outlay for farm income stabilization is approximately four and one half billion dollars, while the food assistance programs excluding the school lunch program are funded to a level of approximately 575 million dollars or one-seventh as much. Some industrial farms receive enormous subsidies. In 1967, the J. G. Boswell Company, for example, received four million dollars from the federal government.[17]

Federal food distribution programs are established within the guidelines of four legislative acts: the Agriculture Adjustment Act of 1949 (Commodity Distribution Program), the National School Lunch Act, the Food Stamp Act of 1964, and the Child Nutrition Act of 1966 (Special Milk Program for Children, Pilot School Breakfast Program and Equipment Program to Initiate or Expand School Food Service). All are administered at the federal level by the United States Department of Agriculture.

The Commodity Distribution Program

The Commodity Distribution Program (or Direct Distribution Program) supplies food to nonprofit school lunch programs, summer camps for children, charitable institutions serving needy persons, and state and local welfare agencies for the distribution of low-income households. Until just recently the items available under the commodity program were limited to such foods as flour, cornmeal, rice, dried peas, raisins and bulgar wheat. Precious little amounts of meat were offered and only on a sporadic basis. No fresh vegetables or fruits were ever offered. If these foods represent the sole source of nutritional intake, as they often do, they do not represent an adequate diet. Indeed the supply usually runs out by the twenty-second or twenty-third day of the month.[18] Under considerable public pressure the range of offerings has been expanded to contain more meat, canned vegetables, evaporated milk and some other items, but the expansion is more theoretical than actual, because the county government can accept or reject whatever it wants and the commodities offered must be in sufficient supply on the market.[19]

The administrative structure of the surplus commodities program is fundamentally unsound. County government has been allowed to have almost sole discretion as to whether a food assistance program is initiated. Because the county must certify applicants, then transport, store and distribute the food (and in New Jersey, for example, pay a 4-percent surcharge to the state for the food itself), all of which represents another cost added onto the already heavy payroll of local government, little stimulus for the program comes from the counties themselves. In many instances, the local government opposes the food assistance program.

The county government's interest in cutting costs at the expense of the politically weakest force—the poor—is then expressed in the quality of the program once it is put into operation. The certification process is often inappropriate and inhumane. Frequently the centers for determining eligibility are open only two or so days a week. The hours are inflexible; if a food crisis occurs or if the card that signifies eligibility is lost, the family must wait until the following week to be recertified, a time lapse which may extend to five days. In the period, the family has few options—the welfare department is not responsive to emergencies unless the family is knowledgeable about its operations and refuses to be intimidated. Thus, the head of the family has three real choices: he may allow his family to go hungry until the center reopens; he may beg; he may steal.

The distribution point for the commodities, especially in the rural areas of America, is frequently limited to the county seat, which is often many miles from the homes of the people who need the food. Transportation costs to and from the site often take a considerable bite out of the already limited financial resources of the family. The recipient must according to the regulations take a month's supply of food, which is sometimes more than the family can adequately store; it either rots or is partially eaten and polluted by vermin. In the summer the commodities are sometimes unloaded off the tailgates of trucks that were used the day before on road work. In the winter distribution sometimes lapses because of transportation difficulties—this while ranchers airdrop hay to cattle stranded by snow storms. The days and hours of distribution are limited and the lines of people waiting for food are long. For the sick, the blind, the infirm, and for female heads of households with many small children the commodities package is too heavy to carry. An average family of four receives approximately one hundred pounds of commodities monthly.[20]

Permeating the administration of the commodity program is the implication that government is doing a favor for the people. There is rarely any effort made to obscure the fact that the giver has all the authority and that the receiver must accept his dole gratefully or accept the consequences. It takes stamina to endure the administrative machinery of this program and the indignity that attends it.

Furthermore, little or no attempt is made to educate the recipients to the importance of supplementing these foods with lean meat and fresh fruits and vegetables or to provide them with recipes which would maximize the potential food value of the products distributed. A vigorous campaign in nutritional education might begin to alleviate the kind of problem uncovered by research among Job Corps enrollees: "Within the first month after enrollment the average Job Corps youth gained 15 pounds. This is a great achievement but sad and damning evidence of the nutritional inequities in the richest and most powerful country in the world." [21]

Perhaps the best solution to the problem would be for the Direct Distribution Program to offer the same foods to low-income people as it does to children through the National School Lunch Program. These foods include apple sauce, green beans, grapes, chopped meat, peaches, peas and corn. Is it too much to expect that such basic staples could be provided to all the poor people in the "richest and most powerful country in the world"?

Food Stamp Program

Although many counties still maintain a commodity program, the Department of Agriculture policy since 1964 has been to phase out commodity distribution and to introduce the Food Stamp Program. The stamp program works in the following way: families exchange the money they would normally spend for food, for stamps worth more. The "bonus"—that is the difference between the amount spent on the stamps and their actual value—is paid by the federal government. The stamps are then used to buy food in retail food stores which have a contract with the Department of Agriculture. In New Jersey banks operate as a "third party"; an individual must purchase his stamps at a bank (the bank receives thirty-five cents per transaction from the government), and the retail grocer turns in his stamp receipts to a bank for credit to his account. If the Food Stamp Program were properly implemented, the negative aspects of the commodity program would be eradicated and the individual could buy the food he and his family needs in a dignified setting.

The operation of the stamp program has never fulfilled its promise. From the very beginning the bonuses made available to the very poor were significantly less than the bonuses allowed to the less deprived poor. The department's dubious rationale was that the very poor would not fundamentally alter their diet, but bootleg the stamps if they were given enough to eat. This, of course, is a policy of enforced hunger. At all levels of income, though, the bonus allotment is insufficient. It does not provide the necessary buying power to purchase an adequate diet even by the Department of Agriculture's own standards.[22] Homer Bigart of *The New York Times* writes of the plight of two families who use the stamps, one from Mississippi and the other from Texas, both representative of the situation with which countless families throughout the nation are confronted:

> In another shack, where daylight could be seen through a corner rathole, a mother with seven children, living on social security payments of $95.40 a month, described her budget. She had to make a cash contribution of $38 to obtain $96 in food stamps and "I run out of food in the third week." [23]
> In worse plight was a Mrs. Espinosa, found with 10 children in another tiny flat. She, too, was getting the maximum $123

monthly welfare payment, out of which she had to invest
$58 to get $128 worth of food stamps and pay $39 rent.
They left only $26 for all other expenses. The family sub-
sisted mainly on tortillas and beans. Three of the children
had no shoes.[24]

The reason that poor families rely on what some people call
"ethnic foods" such as tortillas and pintos, for example, is
not that they prefer these foods. It is because they need
cheap food to fill their stomachs even if it does not provide
proper nutrition. If the poor were to invest in an ideal balanced diet with fruit, vegetables and meat, they would run
out of food even earlier in the month.

As can be seen from the above examples, the Department of Agriculture requires that a family invest as much as
40 or 50 percent of its income for stamps. A middle-class
family ordinarily spends around 18 percent.[25] But in a
poor family money outlay for food must be adjusted to meet
the particular financial circumstances of the month. Rent,
heat and transportation to work are fixed expenses which
must be paid first. What is left goes for food and other
needs. Thus, the high ratio of the cost of the stamps to the
total income per month often deters people from accepting
the program and forces out others who take the chance. Toilet paper, cleanser, soap and cleaning utensils which are
needed to maintain proper sanitation, and are also unavoidable costs, cannot be purchased with stamps and this too
stretches the very limited money left after the purchase of
stamps. Moreover, if a family is unable to get enough
money together on the day the stamps are sold, they must go
without them. Failure to buy stamps two months consecu-
tively forces the family to go through the certification process again. Families with no discernible income or very low
income—and there are a large but unknown number of
these in America especially in the rural areas—are not even

taken into account in the administration of the Food Stamp Program.

Furthermore, certain counties refuse to join the program. This means that many people cannot benefit from the program. Counties refuse to join the program for three reasons. The first is financial: the administrative costs of the program are shared by the federal government and the county (the cost to the county being approximately one-third of the total). The second reason is operational: the counties say that it is extremely difficult to find qualified people to staff the program. And third, there is the lack of "popular" support for the program. The poor have no lobbyists, and are unable to mount a campaign to overcome the resistance of the county administrators. Too many of those eligible have been made to feel that their welfare check is on tenuous ground already and that they dare not risk losing it through protest, no matter how legitimate.

There is, however, one group of low-income people particularly ill-served by both the commodities and stamp programs: the migrant worker and his family. In both programs the problem of residency interferes seriously with the certification process, and both programs contain additional obstacles. It is almost impossible for migrant families to supply the required cash for food stamps, and if able to do so, the migrants' isolated geographical position in rural counties makes it very difficult to reach authorized retail outlets. In addition, the migrant worker is frequently totally restricted in his purchasing options. Collusion between an employer or crew chief and the local grocer results in what amounts to a "company store," with inferior products at high prices and oppressive credit arrangements. The commodities program has improved the delivery system but transportation, storage and cooking problems are especially difficult.

Either because of a misanthropic philosophy on the part

of the Department of Agriculture, or profound mismanagement, or a combination of both, the initiation of the stamp program has added to the nutritional woes of the poor rather than assuaging them. As commodities have been replaced by stamps, thousands of people have been left with no assistance at all. In Mississippi, after eight counties switched to stamps, 32,000 fewer people were getting aid a year later. In Arkansas, only 9,700 families benefit from stamps even though there are 54,531 families on the welfare rolls, and no one believes that the number of people on the rolls represents the total number of poor people. It is disturbing to note that at present there are 6 million people getting food assistance—3 million under each program —while six years ago there were more people being assisted under the original commodities program.[26]

The commodities and food stamp programs are the only efforts being made in America today to provide nutritional security for poor children during the critical stages of development. Obviously, these programs are grossly inadequate. Yet admitting this does not help change the reality of a national disgrace. By federal government criteria, in December, 1968, there were approximately 22 million people living in poverty. As noted, there are approximately 6 million people receiving benefits under both the commodity and stamp programs. Thus, at least 16 million people, women and infants included, are neglected.[27]

National School Lunch Program

The NSLP provides commodity and cash grants to state educational agencies to assist them in providing adequate school lunches. Cash grants are distributed by the state agency for food assistance to schools participating in the program. In 1966, for example, 1,156 New Jersey public schools took part in the program, serving 274,559 children.[28] To be eligible, schools must agree to operate the lunch program on a nonprofit basis, serve nutritious lunches that meet the requirement for "Type A" lunches as established by the Secretary of Agriculture and provide lunches free or at a reduced price to children who are unable to pay the full price.

Although school lunches provided under the National School Lunch Program come too late in life to save a child from damage done to him by malnutrition in earlier years, they could make an essential contribution to an overall effort to provide equal educational opportunity for all. It has been noted time and again that when a hot lunch is offered to disadvantaged children, many of those who were previously colorless, drowsy and largely uneducable become alive, alert and involved in the classroom situation. It is self-evident that "if children are to learn at a maximum rate they cannot be hungry or malnourished." [29] But despite the fact that the National School Lunch Program is a marvelous way to fight hunger, the program is not used to combat the malnutrition of the disadvantaged.

In the National School Lunch Program, the Department of Agriculture provides the states with a cash subsidy which is distributed to the various school districts. At the local level, however, the cost of administration and cooking greatly exceeds the rate of reimbursement, and poor districts are unable to afford the cost. Frequently the schools which have great numbers of disadvantaged students and accept the program elevate the cost of the lunch in order to run the program, and the disadvantaged child can no longer afford it. Although there is legislation which provides for free lunches for needy students, the funding is grossly insufficient. The funds available are maladministered. The National Councils of Catholic, Jewish and Negro Women, the National Board of the Y.M.C.A. and Church Women

United have studied the performance of the National School Lunch Program throughout the nation and have noted in their report, *Their Daily Bread,* that the decision as to who should receive a free lunch is arbitrary and varies from one school to another.[30]

Aspects of the maladministration of the National School Lunch Program discovered by the women's groups are scandalous: in Seattle, Washington, children on welfare are denied free service because theoretically the welfare allotment includes a school lunch. In other areas children who cannot afford either to bring or buy their lunch are often found sitting and watching the others eat. Some schools rotate the free lunches among the poor. Consequently, a child may deny himself meals at home before his scheduled lunch, thus permitting others in his family to eat more. These children become ill or cry from hunger when the schedule suddenly changes or a mix-up occurs. An elementary school principal in Mobile, Alabama, is quoted as saying, "We choose the children for free lunches at the beginning of the year. . . . If you have to go hungry, you might as well get used to it." [31]

The reasons for the low participation of poor children in the National School Lunch Program are numerous. Many ghetto schools are old, and others were built by planners who believed in the concept of the neighborhood school, and thus there are few cafeterias. The neighborhood concept is onerous as regards the nutrition of the poor. The disadvantaged child can't go home for lunch because there is no well-stocked larder for him to go home to. That is part of what it is to be poor. The youngster ends up sharing a bag of potato chips or cheap dessert items and washing them down with a bottle of coke. And malnourished children, as has been known from time immemorial, cannot learn.

There are fifty million public elementary and secondary schoolchildren in America, and eighteen million of them receive a lunch at school.[32] Of the six million poor children only two million receive a free or reduced-price lunch. Two-thirds of the poor children in America, or four million children, do not get a hot lunch at school. Thus eight-tenths of the recipients of the program are not disadvantaged children.[33]

A status report on the operation of the National School Lunch Program in some of the highly volatile urban areas of the United States highlights profoundly distressing facts. In Cleveland, no elementary schools participate; in riot-torn Detroit, 78 slum schools are excluded; none of the ghetto schools in Philadelphia participate; only 9 of 71 schools participate in Minneapolis.[34] Approximately fifty percent of the children in Trenton, Paterson, Jersey City, Camden, Elizabeth and Newark go without a school lunch. All of the neglected children in the New Jersey schools noted above are young, elementary school students whose need for a balanced diet is especially critical.[35] Further, despite the fact that New Jersey is the most heavily urbanized state in the nation, pockmarked with decaying cities, with three or four hundred thousand poor people, it ranks forty-ninth—next to last—among the states of the nation in the percentage of children participating in this program.[36]

There are other programs of the federal government which provide monies to assist in the development of nutrition assistance programs in the schools. Legislation supports expansion of cafeterias and kitchens, and there is a pilot breakfast program and an evening meal program as well. For the vast majority of the poor children of America, however, the legislation is meaningless. It is severely underfunded. For example, in 1968 only two million dollars was allotted to states to expand lunchroom facilities.[37] And the Department of Agriculture in March, 1969, instituted a free food stamp program in two counties in South Carolina. But it, too, is just a pilot project, and the income levels for participation are so restrictive—one must earn less than thirty dollars per month to get free stamps—that very few people benefit.[38]

Man has always been aware of the pernicious effects of hunger on thinking. Our understanding of this phenomenon is now, of course, more sophisticated than it was during the time of Christ or in the middle ages. Contemporary scientists can discuss in great detail the repercussions that malnutrition has on the growth of the brain of a severely malnourished infant or the bio-medical and psychological effects of malnutrition during the early years of life. And many Americans now know, scientists and laymen alike, that there is chronic malnutrition throughout America. What we as a society lack is the will to place nutrition of the poor—pregnant women and children especially—among the highest national priorities. We are unwilling to stop the pain of hunger which poor children suffer; we are unwilling to make a real investment in their human potential. The superabundance of America and our massive national investments in defense and space programs stand in grotesque contrast to the pitiful food assistance programs.

ఌ VIII.

Newark: A Case Study
of Urban Poverty

THE PRECEDING CHAPTERS of this paper have al-
luded often to the "culturally deprived" child who is too
frequently and tragically confused with that child who is
mentally retarded as a consequence of organic factors. The
culturally deprived child is deprived precisely because his
environment isolates him from those stimuli which challenge the middle-class youngster. Concerned with the day-to-
day struggle for survival in the ghetto, undernourished, ill-
clothed, buffeted by noise and by too many brothers, sisters
and relatives in too few rooms, exposed to truancy, delinquency, crime, the ghetto child cannot hope to compete
with his middle-class counterpart and so drops further and
further behind, ultimately to be placed in a Special Education class and labeled "retarded."

Rather than continue with such generalizations, however, it may be easier to understand the plight of this hypo-

thetical child by placing him in a context, the brutality of which need not be hypothesized—Newark, New Jersey.

The approach to Newark from the New Jersey Turnpike is unforgettable, not because of the beauty of that misnamed stretch of land known as "the meadows," but because of the stench in the area. Professor Alan Temko, speaking at the conference sponsored by the New Jersey Association of Architects held at Princeton University in December, 1966, called the meadows land a "stinking morass" [1] and it has undoubtedly provoked even harsher epithets. It may not be too forceful to suggest that were this stench given visible and tangible form it might take on the shape of the Central Ward of Newark, a case study in the ugly facts of poverty.

These facts have received full coverage since the riots of July, 1967. *Life Magazine* repeated these statistics culled from Newark's Model Cities application: "Newark's crime, venereal disease and maternal mortality rates are the highest of all comparable-sized cities in the country, the infant mortality rate the second highest. It has the highest incidence of substandard housing, the lowest per capita income, the highest per capita tax rate. Where the nation's average unemployment rate is 3.2%, Newark's is 8.2%" [2] and the *Newark Evening News,* quoting a spokesman from HUD (Department of Housing and Urban Development), repeated the same statistics, adding that in the ninth to twelfth grades, the dropout rate is 22 percent. Senator Edward Brooke (R., Mass.) drew the conclusion implicit in these facts: "The reason this [the riot] is happening is because the conditions are there. The conditions are such that it can be set off." [3] It may require a riot to generate sufficient concern to meet these conditions, but the burden that ghetto life imposes on a child of the Central Ward is no less tragic than the aftermath of a riot and, unfortunately, a lot less apparent.

The isolation of such a child and his parent was illuminated by an analogy drawn by Professor Temko and pursued by George Rockrise at the Princeton conference cited above.

> Take an infantry man in Vietnam, in trouble; he's carrying a portable radio that costs about $380; he summons a helicopter that costs over $250,000 which promptly sprays that unfortunate country with perhaps $100,000 worth of munitions. With what does a young mother in the slum call for help; where is her radio? Suppose her child has a toothache; where is the traveling dental clinic, instead of that helicopter that costs $250,000? Where is that free medicine that would cost the same as that napalm? [4] . . . When you go into the ghettos in Newark . . . [you] find that the very needs of these people, the very things they require, are so far so primary. It's almost the kind of thing you find when you parachute into a jungle and you say: How do I live; what are the basic tools; I don't have the radio and there is no helicopter. The only enemy is not enemy troops but the natural ecology of the jungle. [5]

This study in Newark's poverty will attempt to translate Temko's and Rockrise's metaphor into facts, the same facts cited by *Life,* amplified and interrelated. The study will be divided into the following seven sections: Background, Neighborhoods, Housing, Family Structure, Health and Welfare, Employment, and Education. But it is necessary to have recorded the metaphor before proceeding. It is significant because it stresses that brutality of ghetto life which facts alone cannot convey. Life in the Central Ward in Newark is primitive; the needs of its inhabitants are primary; and its people are as isolated and as vulnerable as the unarmed infantryman in the Vietnamese jungle.

Background

More than half of Newark's 400,000 citizens are Negroes[6] and the majority of these have arrived within the last twenty years.[7] "As recently as 1950, Negroes constituted a scant 17% of Newark's population. With the rush to the suburbs by whites in the affluent era that followed, and the northward hegira of Negro refugees from Dixie, the black population is now estimated at 50% to 55% and even more, making Newark the only major city in the North, except for Washington, with a Negro majority."[8]

Newark has always been the port of arrival for immigrants, especially Italians, Irish, Jewish and German, but the new immigrants, the Negroes, bring with them a radically different background, and they are entering a radically different world. It has been argued (by New York Mayor John Lindsay, for example) that much of the city's critical welfare problems are attributable to "the influx of relatively unskilled persons . . . from Puerto Rico and the American South."[9] The influx of rural poor into urban areas has created what Lindsay labeled a "mismatch"[10] of people with their environment.

This mismatch and some of its more violent repercussions was fully spelled out by *The New York Times* with reference to Newark and its Negro ghetto residents:

> The Negroes come from the South primarily, with the white man's stamp of inferiority already etched on their faces. They come looking for jobs and there are none for them, for many have left the rural South where they toiled in the fields and they have no other skill. They come searching for an education, especially for their children, and the schools are inadequate. They come looking for decent housing and find homes on which the rent is barely within their means. The next step is the relief rolls and on the way down there are

stops at prostitution, burglary, rape, robbery and, for some, murder.[11]

It would be safe to conclude that the problem is twofold. First, the new in-migrants bring their deprivation with them from the South. "Family disruption, violence, brutality, cheapness of life, lack of love, lack of education, lack of medical facilities," are effects which cannot be wiped out in a single generation.[12] And second, the urban slum, such as Newark's Central Ward, can only reinforce this deprivation.

When the Hackensack Indians sold the site of Newark (the third and oldest city in the nation) to a band of Connecticut settlers in 1666 it was hardly a slum, but such has been its plight for the last half-century at least. Raymond Moley in the *Bethlehem Globe-Times* summarized slum problems in Newark in this manner:

In Newark, the problem of slums has been known for many years. The files of the Newark public library are crammed with material on the subject which runs back to the turn of the century. The old Third Ward was the center of public interest long before there was any considerable migration of Negroes. Crimes, slums and disease prevailed then. In 1946 the housing authority of Newark reported on conditions that are even now the target of comments.

The blight was there. The Negroes from Harlem and the South simply moved into its midst. Areas decayed by neglect compelled a lowering of rentals, which invited the influx of impoverished Negroes. And such cheap living quarters drew inhabitants who were too ignorant to realize that there was also a low limit to employment opportunities. The economy of the Newark area simply could not meet the need of jobs for the people who came to live there.[13]

And a 1946 study of housing in Newark relates the following definition of a Newark slum: "An area where dwellings predominate which, by reason of dilapidation, overcrowding, faulty arrangement or design, lack of ventilation, light or sanitation facilities, or any combination of these factors are detrimental to safety, health or morals." [14] These slums "are characterized not only by dilapidation and obsolescence, but also by the presence of high rates of diseases, crime, dependency and poverty. . . . This complex of slum conditions—substandard housing, high density, squalor —cannot be separated from its concomitant, poverty." [15]

Newark has itemized its deficiencies in a more up-to-date context, however. Its Model Cities application (quoted by *Life* above) confirms all of these points and more. It states flatly that "there is no other major city in the nation where these common urban problems range so widely and cut so deeply." [16]

Two salient points are made in the application. First, "the fine and stable 'neighborhoods' that tend to balance the statistics of crisis in other major cities fall beyond the restricted city limits in Newark in such 'neighborhoods' as South Orange, Maplewood, Short Hills and Essex Fells." [17] Secondly, because Newark is a port city both for goods and immigrants, its turnover of people is high. In-migrants do not always stay long enough to learn marketable trades, even assuming that such opportunities to learn are open to them. Furthermore, Newark's market is primarily for high-skill labor. Consequently, its high unemployment rate is in part the "result of the continuing flow-through . . . of a large, poorly-educated and unskilled population mismatched in a high-skill labor-area." [18] Both of these factors combine to create a city which is largely a ghetto.

There should no longer be any doubt as to why Newark was selected as the case study in urban poverty. Nor should there be any doubt that life in such an environment is unhealthy and stultifying to a child, no matter how high his inherent intelligence. The following sections will document the pejorative components of ghetto life in greater detail.

Neighborhoods

A typical Newark ghetto was described in the following words from a housing survey in Newark:

Unsafe, congested, poorly designed street systems; incompatible land uses; obsolete building types; heavy traffic; lack of recreation area are the most frequently observed signs of inadequacy in residential areas. These are closely followed by overcrowding or improper location of structures, and a lack of parking space. . . . Congested, dilapidated dwellings and a lack of planning which results in inadequate ventilation and sunlight, are conditions that encourage disease and illness. Buildings that are fire hazards and neighborhoods that are conducive to crime and delinquency are all manifestations of slums where the poor are forced to live.[19]

Newark's Model Cities application continues the chronical in a similar manner, detailing the physical problems of the ghetto part of the city. There is an

extensive mixture of often incompatible land uses, an oversupply of ground floor, deteriorated commercial space along all major streets, a large number of severely deteriorated blocks, and a vast medium density residential area of two and three story frame houses which show varying signs of deferred maintenance and deterioration . . . Antiquated public facilities, the lack of open space, the overhead utility lines, the poor street lighting; and the indiscriminate use of streets in grid-iron pattern by all kinds of mixed traffic further contributes to the declining tone of the entire neighborhood.[20]

The density of ghetto population has always been difficult to assess, despite the efficiency of the Selective Service and the census takers. Because the City of Newark experienced early and rapid growth on severely limited land area, open land quickly disappeared; the density of the city's population rapidly became a major problem. The 1960 census records Newark's population at 405,000 or a population density of 17,710 persons per square mile, giving Newark the second highest density among the major cities of the country. This is probably a conservative figure. Newark's actual density may well be considerably higher since 25 percent of Newark's land area consists of meadow land, airports and sea facilities, and because some local estimates place the population figures as high as 415,000.[21]

It must be remembered that these figures refer to the City of Newark as a whole, including commercial and industrial as well as residential space; within the ghetto area of Newark, the population density is undoubtedly much higher. Approximately 62,000 people live in the seventeen-hundred-acre core of the city. According to the Model Cities application, this area contains a disproportionate share of the physical, economic and social problems that beset the city.[22]

Translated into more relevant terms, this density means that the ghetto child is constantly oppressed by people, street noise, physical objects, lack of play space, polluted air and, no less significant, lack of privacy. The middle-class student can sit down at a clean desk in his own room. He has clean paper, freshly sharpened pencils; his younger brothers and sisters have been put to bed in their rooms; the house is relatively quiet. Whether he uses them or not, these conditions are available to him. The ghetto child not only lacks a room of his own, he has no space to himself. Usually numerous younger children are underfoot, because the family very often sleeps in the room they live in, and except for the very youngest they probably all tend to go to bed at the same time. Even if the house is quiet, street noises will continue to intrude and distract, and space is at a premium.

Slum density is partially responsible for physical as well as psychological ills. Not only do contagious diseases spread more rapidly, but carriers of contagious diseases abound.

The most highly publicized of these—and most harmful even beyond their ability to spread disease and filth—are rats.

Newark's rat problem has been labeled "critical" by health officers in that city. Although most urban ghettos are rat-infested, Newark's rat population explodes because of the proximity to the slums of garbage dumps, which are the breeding place of rats. Dr. Aaron A. Haskin, Newark's Health Officer, has suggested that the State of New Jersey itself is partly to blame. He claimed that "the State Highway Department in widening the New Jersey Turnpike in the vicinity of the city's garbage dumps neglected to take precautionary measures before digging through thousands of rat nests." [23] He added that "even the sanitary land fill isn't done according to the state sanitary code."

Before the Highway Department started excavation, the city worked out a set of rules in cooperation with the State Health Department for mass extermination of the rats. City officials recommended that the problem be minimized by circling the area with poison, so that when the rats did start running they would at least have consumed one dose of poison. Dr. Haskin states that the State Highway Department went ahead with its project, ignoring the recommendation. [24]

Housing

Housing in the ghetto neighborhoods of Newark is highly inadequate.

In the 1950 census, 28,260 substandard dwellings were counted in Newark. Of these 18,087 had no bath or shower, 15,939 had no hot water and 8,478 had no flush toilet. Those were typical defects, not the complete list. Yet the average rental was $27 and one-third rented for $40 and up.

The landlords who own 92 percent of Newark's slums collect $8,392,000 a year in rents. They spend practically nothing for maintenance and repairs. They pay meager taxes. Annual returns of 40 to 50 percent on the investment are common and some landlords harvest up to 100 percent a year from slum properties. These hovels are not merely unhealthy. They are unsafe. In Newark, as in every other large city, scores of citizens have burned to death in slum firetraps . . . While the slum landlords are taking in their millions, Newark taxpayers in good neighborhoods and commercial sections are shelling out $6,000,000 a year to pay for special city services to the slums. The subsidy for low-rent housing is insignificant by comparison with this enormous subsidy.[25]

When the above passage was written in 1950, Newark had the highest proportion of dilapidated housing in the nation. It still does. "A slum clearance program has helped somewhat but it has barely touched the worst ghetto—the Central Ward." [26] In 1962, 32.6 percent of the city's housing was substandard [27] and the percentage in the ghetto must have been at least twice as high.

Newark's Model Cities application, despite its attempts to sound optimistic about the amount of public housing developed in Newark within the last decade, admits that the problems of providing adequate housing for the ghetto area are almost insurmountable. "Deterioration, however, continues to spread. Portions of Newark are currently under the severe threat of environmental conditions which, in a few more years, could result in uninhabitable conditions" [28] and it recommends "the massive restoration of entire neighborhoods." [29]

Part of the problem is certainly attributable to the fact that most of Newark's housing is in the form of old or rapidly aging frame structures. Over 80 percent are forty or more years old. But the major cause of Newark's housing problems was detailed in a book published at Rutgers University last year. The result of an intensive study of the city's slums, largely centered on its housing, *The Tenement Landlord,* by Professor George Sternlieb, echoed the 1950 housing study in placing the blame for Newark's housing in part on the slum landlord. Briefly, as related by Raymond Moley in the *Bethlehem Globe-Times,* Sternlieb shows that

> Over the past 20 years the Newark tax rate per $100 of valuation has more than doubled.
>
> The broad impact of property taxation is not the real question. The vital point is that assessments and the consequent burden rise only when owners improve their property. Here Sternlieb produces incontestable evidence which justifies his conclusion: "In the face of rent level plateaus, the increasing level of the tax rate, which Newark and many other municipalities have found necessary, has reduced the profitability of slum investment." In simpler language he says, "The typical landlord response has been to reduce maintenance and avoid additional investment."
>
> In even simpler language, the conclusion is that present assessment and tax rates slap a penalty on the owner who improves or rebuilds his housing. And since that is true, the landlord receives a subsidy when he permits his property to disintegrate.[30]

Whoever is to blame—the landlord, tenant, aged building, an absurd tax system—the victim is regrettably the same. The slum child still has to live in that over-forty-year-old frame building, poorly lighted, poorly maintained, overcrowded, lacking sanitary facilities, and without the privacy of the middle-class home.

Families

One of the country's best-known urban experts, Daniel Patrick Moynihan, has advanced the thesis that there are certain signs which foretell the formation of an "urban under-class," a class which is so deprived, especially when compared with the society which surrounds it, that its members have in effect dropped out of society altogether; their main impulses are only destructive. It is these people whom Oscar Lewis has described as living in a "culture of poverty," and one of the signs of such a culture, Moynihan argues, is the disorganized or broken family.[31]

According to Census of Housing figures for the year 1960, 27.5 percent of Newark's nonwhite families had female heads. This rate has clearly risen in the last seven years, since Aid to Dependent Children cases alone have tripled between 1960 and 1966.[32] Birth rates reflect the same lack of family structure. "Almost one of every four babies born to Newark residents last year was illegitimate." [33] According to the Newark Health Department's 1966 health report, 2,336 babies out of 10,001 were reported as born out of wedlock.[34] Newark's out-of-wedlock births are increasing particularly among teenagers. A city hospital report on 1,739 illegitimate births revealed that 20 percent of these mothers were under seventeen years of age. The Newark Board of Education reported 312 cases of pregnancy among teenage children for the same year.[35]

As might be expected, these figures are reflected on the welfare rolls. In 1960, the Essex County ADC office handled a caseload of 3,300; by 1967, the load had tripled to 10,000 cases. Newark's ADC families usually present 88–89 percent of Essex County's cases.[36]

> The steady and rapid rise of ADC cases cannot be attributed solely to economic factors. They also seem to reflect the effects of inimical social factors at work. The age of the mothers, when first applying for ADC, is growing younger. In 1960, only 30 percent of new applicants to the ECWB-ADC program were mothers of 25 years of age and younger.

By 1964, the proportion rose to 47 percent. Furthermore, out-of-wedlock births and unwed mothers as heads of households, as well as unwed mothers under 16 years of age are on the increase. Disorganized or broken homes—divorced, abandoned, and putative fathers absent from homes—and its [sic] consequences, constitute 80 percent of the reasons given on the application for assistance, with 45 percent of the group claiming the absence from home of the putative fathers as the reason for their economic needs.[37]

A family from which the father is missing or in which there is a series of "fathers" does not provide a stable atmosphere for a child, particularly when the rest of his environment is unhealthy. If this is the only life he knows, he has no alternative experience upon which to base his adult behavior. The brief and unbelievable textbook contact with Dick and Jane's happy family complete with father and dog cannot mitigate the effects of generations of fatherless families.

Health and Welfare

The physical health of the culturally deprived child can radically affect his mental health. And one of the most immediate factors affecting a child's school performance is hunger. It is worth repeating some of the statistics quoted earlier in this paper. In the National School Lunch Program, New Jersey ranks forty-ninth—next to last in providing hot lunches for its children during school hours. A 1965 study indicated that nearly half the children in Newark did not benefit from the National School Lunch Program.[38]

The family of this hypothetical child may be similarly deprived of those programs which exist to supplement the inadequate diet of the poor. Essex County refused the Food Stamp Program which is slowly replacing Direct Distribution of Food (federal regulations prohibit an area from participating in both programs), and Newark's Direct Distribution Program functions in a manner which might charitably be described as haphazard. Only one-quarter of Newark's poor who are eligible for this program actually participate in it. The program, when it is administered, is operated by the Senior Citizens Commission. The centers for determining eligibility are open only two mornings per week, and there is no procedure to allow for emergencies. Families to whom these crises occur must starve until the following Tuesday or Thursday.[39]

Newark exhibits other health hazards beyond poor nutrition. According to 1966 statistics, this city has the highest mortality rate, the highest maternal mortality rate, the highest infant mortality rate, the highest rate of new tuberculosis cases, and the highest rate of venereal disease in the country. The most recent report on air pollution conducted by the U. S. Public Health Service on a national sample of 302 cities rated Newark ninth highest.[40]

With respect to infant and maternal mortality:

Newark had a 1966 rate of 33.9 per thousand live births, against a New Jersey State rate of 23.3 and a national rate of 24.8. Newark's high rate can be attributed to a combination of causes, including: large number of out-of-wedlock births—a rate of 20.2 against a U.S. rate of 6.0; a high percentage of teenage unwed mothers—over 300 school-age children annually reported pregnant by Newark's Board of Education; the generally poor physical condition of young mothers; their failure to seek prenatal care through ignorance of prenatal care need, or of the existence and availability of such services; or as a result of trying to prevent discovery of condition. . . . The same factors undoubtedly contribute to the national leading rate of maternal deaths in Newark. Against a New Jersey State rate of 0.4 per thousand live births, Newark's rate of 1.4 is three and a half times as high.

Newark's general conditions . . . contribute their own share to these statistics, as indicated by Newark's death rate for all causes of 12.8 per thousand, in contrast to a U.S. rate of 9.4 per thousand [1965 statistics].[41]

The high rate of tuberculosis—108.2 per 100,000 cases as against a national rate of 25.3 [42]—is in part a consequence of environmental conditions and partly a consequence of the largely immigrant population from rural areas. Tuberculosis is a slum disease. It is spread only by germs and germs flourish in foul areas. In 1950, the lowest rate of TB cases was in the well-maintained Vailsburg section of Newark. The highest rate was seven times the city average and nineteen times the Vailsburg rate—in the Fourth Ward, a slum area.[43]

The rate of venereal disease, like the TB rate which is already the highest in the nation, is increasing rapidly. In 1964, 751 cases were reported; in 1965, the figure had nearly doubled to 1,185. And it is generally accepted that for every VD case reported there are five to ten which are unreported. According to the U. S. Public Health Service, in 1965, Newark had a rate of 86.9 per 100,000 population. The New Jersey state rate was 14.0; the national rate was 12.2.[44]

Nor should it be assumed that statistics on VD are any less relevant to the hypothetical slum child than are figures on nutrition, infant and maternal mortality, and tuberculosis. "Data on 109 teenagers attending Paterson and Newark VD clinics from Dec. 1963 to Dec. 1964, revealed that 14 of them were only 10–14 years old." [45]

Newark certainly has other health problems—air pollution, drug addiction (Newark ranks seventh among the ten leading cities in the country in drug addicts) and alcoholism[46] among them—but these are too detailed to develop adequately here.

Despite these obviously mounting health needs, Newark has been undergoing a decline in health facilities and health services. "One hospital, located in the heart of the core city, moved to the suburbs. This same area . . . has seen a reduction of forty percent in the number of doctors between 1951 and 1964." [47]

Nor are the welfare services adequate to the health needs of the poor in Newark. "In general, both the City Administration and its community agencies, public and private alike, are experiencing a dwindling financial base in the face of a rising demand for essential services." [48] Newark's high marriage rate (10.3 per thousand population), high birth rate (26.2 per thousand for all of Newark and 32.0 per thousand for the core city, contrasted with a U.S. birth rate of 19.4), and the continuing large influx of young Negro and Puerto Rican families have strained the city's resources far beyond its ability to provide for its poor. [49]

As of September, 1966, 13.7 percent of Newark's total population was receiving some form of welfare. The ADC program, largest of the public assistance categories, served an average of 4.2 persons per family (or three-plus children per family). [50] This burden is intensified by "a State legislature that refuses to consider adding the federal cost-sharing ADC-UP classification." [51]

The numbers on welfare tell little with respect to mental health, but the crippling social effects of an outmoded and humiliating welfare system on the parents and children involved are real. "The present system imposes a cruel cost on individuals." [52] Not only does it humiliate those "who are clearly unemployable but must keep up a pretence of applying for jobs in order to safeguard their meager dole," [53] but also it penalizes those who are able to work. "The popular feeling is that an individual on relief should accept any job. But there is small gain when a man is forced into a job paying too little for family maintenance." [54] As one welfare recipient remarked of a job offer, "With that job, I'd still be on welfare . . . but with no chance to look for a decent job." [55] Nor does the fact that new arrivals are ineligible for aid, this in a city of transients, make any more sense. "To be admitted to the welfare rolls in Newark, an applicant must prove two years of residence in the State, one year in the county, and one year in the city. The length of residence at various addresses is verified by landlords." [56]

Newark lacks the financial resources to provide the kind of intensive, long-range training and rehabilitation services which many of its citizens require before they can begin to seek employment; furthermore, the City Department of Welfare is prohibited by state regulations from supplying such training.[57] As indicated in the earlier chapter on welfare, many individuals are classified as employable when they are clearly unfit, simply because there are no other alternatives.

Employment

A discussion of welfare cannot help but touch on the related problem of the poor and employment. Given Newark's high proportion of nonwhite, mobile, immigrant, unskilled and poorly educated population, mismatched in a high-skill labor area, the city's employment problems should be apparent. Newark's rate of unemployment has been persistently twice as high or higher than the national average. The exact figure is hard to pinpoint accurately. Estimates range from 8.2 percent to 14 percent. The national rate is 3.2 percent.[58]

A clearer indication of Newark's unemployment rate relative to other cities of the nation is the fact that "since 1964, Newark has been first an ARA [Area Redevelopment Act]—and now an EDA [Economically Depressed

Area]—designated area." [59] The classification is based on rate of unemployment; only four other cities in the nation are so designated—Oakland, San Diego, Miami and Camden, New Jersey.

The mismatch between people and jobs is not the sole cause of unemployment in Newark. In a recent article in the *Newark Star-Ledger,* the director of the New Jersey State Employment Office revealed that numerous incidents of discrimination have been reported, and that "possibly hundreds of Negro job applicants were quoted lower rates of pay after appearing in person for job interviews." [60]

Furthermore, "in Newark's top fifteen businesses, only ten to fifteen percent of the employees are Negroes, despite the city's fifty-one percent Negro population." [61]

Further statistics cited in the same article revealed that only 3.7 percent of white-collar jobs in Newark are held by Negroes, although those jobs constitute 80 percent of Newark's job market. Only 7.9 percent of the blue-collar jobs are held by Negro employees, and in Newark's largest industries Negroes are equally under-represented. Chemical industries employ only 6.7 percent; electrical industries only 10.3; insurance carriers only 3.4; nonelectrical machinery only 7.3; and medical services only 26 percent.[62]

At the same time 10 to 12 percent of all of the city's Negroes are unemployed. In the ghetto, 17 percent are unemployed and 22 percent of those between the ages of seventeen and twenty-one are unemployed.[63] Meanwhile, the greater portion of persons employed in Newark are commuters (about 300,000 every day; Newark's population is 400,000), while only a very small number of Negroes commute to jobs in the suburbs.

Whether the mismatch of people and jobs, or perhaps discrimination, is to blame for Newark's relief rolls, the welfare statistics summarize an ominous tale for the city's citizens. A study of the 745 welfare recipients conducted by

Rutgers revealed the following: of the 745 participants, 78 percent were Negro, 13 percent were Puerto Rican, and 9 percent were white. Stated place of birth supports the above analysis of Newark's impoverished population as predominantly immigrant. Fifty-six percent were born in one of the Southern states; 13 percent in Puerto Rico; 14 percent elsewhere in the state or county. Only 16 percent were born in Newark. A related study noted that 62 percent of the heads of families among such recipients were under forty years of age. Of these more than 50 percent had eight years or less of schooling. And at least 16 percent were functionally illiterate.[64]

Public Education*

The Newark public schools, which are representative of inner-city schools throughout the nation, face almost overwhelming difficulties. They are failing to educate the children who attend them.

Ethnic groups within the system are segregated and will remain so for the foreseeable future. For September, 1967, it was predicted that K-12 enrollment would be approximately seventy-eight thousand students. Close to 80 percent would be minority group children: 65 percent Negro and 15 percent Puerto Rican. This prediction was generally accurate and the situation has not markedly improved. Significantly and obviously the 20 percent white children remain safely outside the heart of the inner city. The white children are almost totally isolated from the minority-group children. There are seventy-five school buildings in Newark—thirteen are attended predominately by white students. The re-

---

* All statistical information on the Newark Public School System is taken from the Newark Model Cities application.

maining sixty-two are attended by populations that are at least 51 percent minority children. Thirteen schools will be attended by very close to 100 percent minority group—the percentage of white students varies *from 0.01 to 0.9 percent*.

The faculty of the Newark school system, relative to suburban teachers, are poorly trained and not highly motivated to educate disadvantaged children. One-fifth of the faculty, or approximately six hundred teachers, are classified as substitutes. These teachers are not permanently certified by the State of New Jersey and/or have not taken or have not passed an examination required by the Newark Board of Education. The financial and social status of these substitutes further mitigates against their playing a positive role in the classroom. The job of substitute teacher is not a highly respected position within the education system itself. A substitute's salary is $5,500 per year. There are no fringe benefits, no tenure and no pay grade credit for time served in that capacity.

The possibilities for upgrading the skills of teachers is severely limited by the teacher-Board of Education contract which legally allows the staff to leave the school at 3:30 P.M. Teachers are required to stay after 3:30 only one day a month for staff meetings. Of course, in-service training could take place if the Board of Education were able to pay teachers to stay after school. The Board, however, does not have the money.

Beyond the fact that the school buildings are old, unhealthy and unsafe, there is an appalling lack of space per student. At present the elementary schools are the most crowded and lack space for six thousand children. It is estimated that in September, 1967, this number will approach nine thousand. The only alternative available is to put students on part-time sessions. Clearly these circumstances do not provide an atmosphere in which cultural deprivation can be alleviated. Lack of space curtails the possibility of social and cultural enrichment programs. Physical limitations have restricted the development of special programs for mentally, physically retarded, and handicapped children. Little, too, can be done to raise the low educational levels of these children's parents; since educational level is a leading factor in the adaptation to urban living and in the ability to understand and to deal effectively with the institutional structure of the city, the child is not rescued from the vicious cycle which has captured his parents.

The student population is highly mobile and characterized by vast numbers of children with special problems—social, psychological, cultural, health, economic—which require individual attention and extensive supportive services. The highest pupil turnover rates are in the elementary schools—and the elementary years are those in which stability is most needed, particularly by children whose home life is chaotic. According to Board of Education figures, approximately one-third of the school population are new arrivals from outside Newark, while approximately 28 percent of the school population annually transfers out of the city's school system.

The inadequacies of Newark's public school system are clearly reflected in the poor achievement levels of its children. In tests administered in October, 1964, in fifty Newark elementary schools, third-grade pupils were reading six months below the national norm and sixth graders in forty-six elementary schools were one year and four months below the national norm. Seventh graders tested at the same time in arithmetic were one year and seven months below the national norm.[65] In 1966, half of the third-grade pupils in the city were still reading six months below the national norm, while half of the pupils in the sixth grade were a year and one-half below this norm. Of the sixteen elementary schools in the inner city, all schools at the third-grade level were below the national norm and twelve were below the city norm.

Recent data from the Bureau of Attendance reflects disciplinary as well as scholastic problems—truancy, pupil transience, dropouts, pregnancies, suspension, vandalism, assaults. There were eleven thousand cases of truancy (14.6 percent of the total school population). Five thousand families moved and 1,576 (9.5 percent) high school students dropped out. Cases of pregnancy totaled 312 and suspensions totaled 750. The County Youth House and Jamestown Reformatory absorbed 474 children. At the same time there were thirty-five hundred cases of children lacking clothing or food (not due to parental neglect) and the Attendance Bureau supplied 850 pairs of shoes.

Cases of arson, school vandalism, false alarms, bomb scares and thefts reached 640, and there were five hundred offenses relating to persons—as assaults, disorderly conduct, alcohol, extortion. If a ghetto child in Newark does not see enough of disorganized and chaotic life and crime at home, he will get a full education in it at school.

IX.

The Migrants:
A Case Study
of Rural Poverty

WHATEVER ELSE may be said about conditions in the ghettos of Newark, Trenton, or other New Jersey cities, it is undeniable that they lie exposed before the public in all their brutal ugliness. If this was not the case before the violence of the summer of 1967, it is certainly the case now. A saving grace about urban poverty is that the explosion it often produces guarantees that it will not remain hidden forever.

But there is a silent, a more secret and a more insidious form of poverty in New Jersey which destroys human minds and human lives without producing any significant impact on the attention or the conscience of the public. This is the poverty of the state's farm laborers. It is the poverty of the migrant stream, of the "tar-paper curtain," of "side-roads

America"—the poverty of those who have made New Jersey the "Garden State" without sharing any of its wealth. It is rural poverty at its worst, and those who experience it rank with the Indians and the Appalachians at the absolute bottom of the American economic heap.

"Migratory farm laborers move restlessly over the face of the land," noted the President's Commission on Migratory Labor in 1951, "but they neither belong to the land nor does the land belong to them. They pass through community after community, but they neither claim the community as home nor does the community claim them. . . . As crops ripen, farmers await their coming; as the harvest closes, the community with equal anxiety awaits their going." [1] New Jersey, which ranks among the top dozen states in its use of farm workers with twenty-four thousand,[2] is an excellent example of this attitude. Desperate for additional workers in 1966, New Jersey growers nevertheless could not rise above the behavior they had shown years earlier, when they "applauded enthusiastically" the characterization of migrants as "bums and drunkards." [3]

The way the migrant is damaged psychologically—the incredible psychic damage done on New Jersey's farms—does not awaken the public as does the drama posed in Newark in summer, 1967. But so isolated, so rootless and so defeated is the migrant that his continued submission is an inherent feature, and a tragic element, of the migratory system. By the age of twenty, writes Robert Coles, migrants "have lost much of their interest in the possibilities of another kind of life. . . . apathy, gloom, and severe depressions are seen in many migrants, and depressions severe and crippling enough to be considered psychotic." [4] The degree to which migrancy can break the spirit is exemplified by the outlook of the migrant himself: "You takes what the bossman gives you . . . when the field is picked clean here and there ain' nothin' else lef' to do, you moves on somewhere else, up the road." [5]

But if the conditions of the migrant's life have made it convenient to villify or to ignore him, the very severity of those conditions have made them almost impossible to describe adequately. Statistics only begin to tell the story:

> Despite the migrant's vital function, his earnings are at the lowest level in our entire economy. Through the combination of low wages and frequent unemployment or underemployment, his earnings for the entire year 1963 averaged only $868. Included in this figure is $211 earned during an average of 17 days of nonfarm work. Farm jobs provided the migrant with only 110 days' work during the year. Because the migrant farmworker family often includes several wage earners, the foregoing figures might be thought to exaggerate the low level of the migrant's actual income. In fact, however, the available data of family earnings are more shocking still. In 1961, in households with three or more farm wage workers, the total year's earnings of these family members together averaged only $1,432. This is less than half the $3,000 income level below which families are commonly considered to be living in poverty.[6]

The average hourly income of farm laborers is less than half that of industrial workers. In 1966, the farm average was $1.09, as compared with a factory average of $2.64.[7] In some areas of the country the farm average was considerably less—incomes of nineteen or twenty cents an hour were reported in one study.[8] Yet, in spite of these alarming figures, the New Jersey Governor's Task Force on Migrant Farm Labor pointed out that "of the 175 municipalities that do not participate in State Aid for General Assistance, 150 are expected to have migrant workers at some time during the growing season." [9]

Another set of statistics, not surprisingly, accompany

these. In a study of the nutritional problems of migrant families, "it was found that 22 families (63 percent) ate no green or yellow vegetables, and 13 families (37 percent) ate less than half the recommended allowance. Seventeen families (48 percent) fell below half the recommended allowance in consumption of citrus fruits and tomatoes, and 12 families (34 percent) ate nothing from this food group. Thirty-four families (97 percent) fell below half the recommended allowance for milk and milk products." [10] Typical health statistics show that "66 percent of migrants in Minnesota aged 15 or more had positive tuberculin tests as compared with only 31 percent for the general population," and that among migrants in Fresno, California, "one half the families had no family doctor; 87 percent had no health insurance; 59 percent of the children under 3 years had not received immunization against diphtheria, whooping cough, tetanus, or smallpox." [11]

New Jersey is not without disturbing figures of its own. In its 1966 Annual Report, the Department of Health revealed that of thirty-nine maternal cases, "two patients had Caesarean Sections, two had partial bilateral salpingectomies, one had an emergency hysterectomy due to a ruptured uterus. One patient with a diagnosis of anemia, had three prenatal admissions and received four pints of whole blood. Two other patients were treated for anemia and one had a reactive serologic test for syphilis." [12] It was also reported that "fifty percent of the migrant camps in the state were sampled for potable water. In 17 percent of those sampled, contaminated water was discovered. Only one-third of the contaminated supplies were retested and half of these were still contaminated." [13]

The migratory life is only dimly revealed through such statistics, however. The nature of the problem can be seen somewhat more clearly through the examination of individual cases. The migrant ministry, for example, reported that

Many of our migrant families have no other home than their old car. A family of 11 had been living in their car for 3 months, from December to March 1958. Included in the family was a 3-month-old baby and another 2 years of age and the rest from 4 years to 14. The older children were 2 years behind their age level in school. All suffered from malnutrition and were unbearably dirty. One family living in their car had been without food for several days. When we investigated, we found five children, the mother and father, asleep in the car and two children crowded in the trunk with the lid down.[14]

Such a case provides an interesting insight into another type of American mobility—a mobility which allows for no real home other than the vehicle, and which is purely geographical rather than social or economic in its implications.

Truman Moore, in "Slaves for Rent," described an even more serious case:

Three hundred migrants were stranded in Nevada when the harvest was late. "For days they had barely enough food to keep alive," the Associated Press reported. "They camped—men, women, and children—in the open, along ditch banks, without protection from winter rains and freezing night temperatures. They took their drinking water from irrigation ditches used by cattle. Many children were sick. And they had no work."

Moore goes on to state that "migrant workers are often housed with the livestock," [15] a situation which has its parallel in New Jersey in the use of converted chicken coops. It is not difficult to see why, during the 1940's, prisoners of war, as well as convicts, were used by the growers.[16]

The typical story of the East Coast migrant, in New Jersey, is hardly more pleasant than those elsewhere. Ben H. Bagdikian describes the case of the Mason family:

After driving day and night for two days, eating hamburgers and hot dogs along the way, they arrived in Cedarville, New

Jersey. They had $14 left. They discovered that the New Jersey strawberry crop was unexpectedly ten days late. They lived in the shacks by the strawberry fields and eked out their $14. . . . After strawberries, their favorite Jersey crop, came the hated onion which needs slashing with a knife. In late August they headed back South, arriving at the broken door of the Florida shack with $3 to show for the summer's work.[17]

If this incident illustrates the degree to which migrants are at the mercy of the crop and the weather, other New Jersey cases demonstrate their dependence on an often heartless community. *The New York Times,* reporting on a hearing on migrant labor, described the kind of incident which is common but rarely publicized: "Another witness, Felix Navarro, a Puerto Rican migrant who spoke through an interpreter, testified that his diabetic wife, Sofia, was turned away from a hospital in Milville and died the next day."[18] But the callousness does not end with death. In a *Newark News* article entitled "Migrant Workers' Lot Better," it was revealed that the death of a small child of New Jersey migrants produced this response:

. . . the local welfare director refused to pay for the child's funeral, saying among other things that the couple should have enough money to pay themselves, that they were "Catholic and had too many children" and the father probably spent his money on drinks. . . . the agent finally paid for the burial but then treated the child as solely a public concern and did not even notify the parents when the burial would be. They did not find out where their child was buried until five days later.[19]

It is almost impossible to translate such incidents into a suitable description of the overall migrant condition. Groping for words, Michael Harrington has written of "a sight of near medieval poverty in the midst of lush abundance."[20] Bagdikian says of migrants that "they live in the worst

squalor, the most hopeless family chaos, and the most ignored poverty of the American poor." [21] And Dale Wright
has called the migrant "the sickest, most depressed, yet least-
known member of the nation's work force." [22]

But Wright also provides an insight into why it is impossible to know and to describe the migrant. To him, the eyes
of a migrant speak these words: "What right have you . . .
to attempt to crawl into my skin, to ask about my woman
and my babies? You know nothing of who we are—or *why*
we are what we are. You know nothing of our kind of
suffering, or of our kind of fears." [23] Robert Coles, stand-
ing on his side of the barrier, has recognized the same problem. "It is hard with words alone," he has written, "to do
justice to the grease and starch, the common lack of utensils, the consequent vitamin deficiencies suffered by people
whose diet ignores food picked by their very hands and rich
as is possible in vitamins." "And so," he concludes, "there is
no comparing the unstable, disorganized social life of migrants with that of the large majority of Americans. They
are separated from us by their hand-to-mouth existence,
their migratory habits which deprive them from intimacy
with any solid residential condition, and, in the case of the
majority of them, Negroes or Puerto Ricans or Mexicans,
by their racial handicaps in our country." [24] One is inclined
to despair of a real understanding and to say, as did John
Steinbeck years ago, that "There is a crime here that goes
beyond denunciation. There is a sorrow here that weeping
cannot symbolize." [25]

There are ways in which the problem can be approached, however. One is to discuss the migrant situation
in terms of a number of disturbing ironies. The most obvious, of course, is the striking example provided by the migrants of poverty in a land of plenty. But there are others.
The conditions of migrancy stand as a sharp refutation of
the Jeffersonian yeoman ideal and the traditional American

"myth of the Garden." Far from serving as the bulwark of a democratic system, the experience of the migrant has demonstrated the flaws in the workings of that system. Cruelly exploited by grower and crew leader, the migrant is excluded from almost all the benefits of his society.

Though vital to the economy of the states in which he works, his lack of residency bars him from voting, from welfare, from adequate education for his children, from health services, from legal protection and, in many areas, from most labor legislation—minimum wage, child labor, workmen's compensation, wage payment, the right to collective bargaining, and unemployment compensation. At the same time, though migrants "are the most interstate workers in the country," [26] they are also excluded from most federal programs. The irony of the migrants' mobile situation is typified by his effective disenfranchisement: "Only in a minority of States is it possible for absent residents both to register and to vote by mail. Accordingly, migrancy is likely to disenfranchise the farmworker in his home State without conferring the right to vote elsewhere." [27] Another irony is that migrant workers who hold United States citizenship are even less well treated than migratory noncitizens working in this country. "Most foreign workers work under contracts that contain benefits more favorable than those generally given to domestic migrants." [28]

The migrant is not only shunted off from one state to another and ignored by the federal government, he is excluded from the very concept of the welfare state. "Here, even more than in the cities," writes Harrington, "the welfare state is for the middle class and the rich. The impoverished who dwell in the pastures of plenty have simply been left out." [29] Harrington notes a further irony: so removed is the migrant from the rest of society that no one is even certain how many migrants there are.[30] In the age of the computer, in the age of the omniscience of the Selective Service

System, it is regrettable to observe the validity of the often-stated paradox that the government knows more about migratory birds than about migratory people.

The suffering of the migrant, moreover, illustrates the hollowness of the promise of upward mobility and the efficacy of hard work. Few people labor as long or as hard as the migrant and yet few are more trapped in the cycle of poverty. "Downward mobility . . . is the prevailing route to farm wagework." [31] In keeping with traditional myths, the migrant tends to blame himself for his own failure, but, notes Coles, "particularly unfortunate is such self-accusation when, in point of fact, these migrant families are willing to move about so far and wide, working so hard." [32] If the migrant is unable to take advantage of welfare or compensation during his periods of unemployment and underemployment, he should at least be spared the scorn given to the welfare recipient. The opposite is the case, however. "Our agricultural system has made harvest work shameful," writes Moore. "It has made the welfare check often more honorable than harvest work." [33]

But perhaps the greatest irony of the migrant situation is the way in which his plight is related to technological advance. The dilemma of the migrant, observes Harrington, "has been created by progress. . . . the farm poor were caught in their own past, the double victims of technology: exiled from their home by advances in agricultural machinery; unfitted for life in the city because of the consequences of industrial mechanization." [34] And yet the New Jersey Farm Labor Report of 1966 disclosed that "mechanization of crop harvest has made its greatest headway on crops where selectivity and handling care are of minor importance." [35] Apparently there is still something to be said for the human being in comparison to the machine even if, in the case of the migrant, he is its victim.

The term "sweatshops in the sun" is an accurate reflection of the paradox of migrancy. Living and working under conditions which were "legislated out of existence in other sectors of American society many years ago," [36] the migrant has departed completely from the old American agricultural ideal. "If anything characterizes the history of the seasonal farm worker, it is this—fate, through famine or depression, war or revolution, has time and again delivered to the commercial grower an ample supply of cheap and docile labor." [37] New Jersey, with some of the largest farm complexes in the nation, provides ample evidence of this bitter truth.

New Jersey has its own special ironies, however—even aside from those made possible by the use of the "Garden State" nickname—for New Jersey regards itself as a prime example of enlightened treatment of the migrant worker. "I am proud," wrote a high state official "of our State's leadership in this area over the past two decades." [38] But the fact is that conditions among migrants have been allowed to deteriorate behind a veneer of humanitarianism.

The programs authorized by the Migrant Labor Act of 1945 have never operated effectively. The hub of the Act, the Migrant Labor Board, was a disappointment from the outset. "The MLB did not start with the characteristic zeal of a new regulatory agency. Its members seemed very concerned about not rubbing farmers the wrong way." [39] And the response of the Secretary of Agriculture to an attempt to provide a minimum of hot-water facilities for migrants was: "In our haste to become the best state on migrant labor policies, we are pushing too hard." [40] Nor was the director of the Office of Economic Opportunity any more anxious to anger the growers. In response to grower complaints that the OEO was luring workers from the field to train them for decent jobs, the director indicated that while he hoped to provide workers with an "occupational option," the training project was "specifically designed to keep the workers on their jobs as long as possible." [41]

New Jersey's leadership in the area of aid to migrants is largely an illusion created by the existence of agencies, rather than of achievements. The Bureau of Migrant Labor, responsible for the enforcement of the Migrant Labor Code, has been conspicuous for its inactivity. The Migrant Health Program, faced with an alarming number of birth complications, has responded by asking in helpless despair, "Is early prenatal clinic care a realistic goal for expectant mothers constantly on the move?" [42] And the Department of Education, in operating summer schools for migrant children, has had this impact on their capabilities to educate the underprivileged: "One would imagine that after *twenty* years of running a migrant school program, the State Department would have enough experience (combined with its own expertise) to draw up some clear guidelines in this area [curriculum]. The truth of the matter is that no such material exists." [43]

But it was not until the summer of 1966 that the full scope of the neglect of the migrant became known. The director of the anti-poverty agency in the leading agricultural counties of Cumberland, Salem and Gloucester was quoted as stating that "he had visited migrant camps in the midwest and west coast and had never seen conditions as bad as those in New Jersey." [44] A Monmouth County official "described the migrants' health standards as 'incredibly inferior.' " [45] And an official of the NAACP, visiting a Cedarville farm, said conditions were "just like 'Tobacco Road.' " [46]

The presence of union organizers and Vista Volunteers —who were active in southern New Jersey briefly, but who will not be back in the foreseeable future—produced a potent backlash on the part of growers. One grower evicted the volunteers from his farm. Another blocked the recruitment of migrant children for the summer school, saying, "If they start going to school, who's going to pick my onions?" [47] But the uproar produced a reaction of its own, and the Governor's Task Force came into being.

Using disturbingly muted language, the Task Force stated that "the general living conditions for too many seasonal farm workers in New Jersey are still far from satisfactory." [48] It outlined deficiencies in statutory provisions, in enforcement, and in institutional and community response for the whole range of migrant problems—from sanitation ("garbage and refuse in migrant camps have been allowed to accumulate in the open without burial or other disposal") [49] to child care ("pre-school age migrant children are frequently left in the care of their older brothers and sisters at the camps, or in the care of aged and infirm persons. In many instances, the infants are actually brought into the fields where their mothers are working").[50] But the most startling aspect of the report was the indicated need to include what seemed an entirely new concept for the state: "All of the above recommendations enumerated in this section are based on the premise which views migrants first and foremost as free men and human resources that ultimately are to be integrated into the totality of community services. Until there is greater community acceptance than presently exists, it is the consensus of the Task Force that special services are not only warranted, but also required as a matter of fundamental humanitarianism." [51] The response? The New Jersey Farm Bureau has sold "no trespassing" [52] signs, at one dollar each, to most of its four thousand members.

But paradox alone does not tell the whole story. A second approach is to consider the migrant as a distinct subculture in American society. The most obvious feature of his subculture is poverty—but poverty more extreme than that known by most poor people. As one farm manager said of migrants, "whoever they are, they're always the people who, come spring, are the hungriest. *Who else wants to work that hard for that little money?"* [53]

Beyond severe poverty, migrants bear all the burdens of membership in racial and ethnic minorities. It is not at all irrelevant, for example, to note that "if in past decades all agricultural programs had been administered without discrimination, many Negro migratory farm workers would have been able to stay at home on their own land." [54] Once in the migrant stream, the onus of race is often as important as that of migrancy. The heavy Negro migrant population of Northampton County, Virginia, shares the deprivations of the large resident Negro population: "Separate analysis of instructional costs per white pupil and per Negro pupil at the elementary level reveals that this county stands fourth in expenditure per white pupil and ninety-fourth in expenditure per Negro pupil among the state's 100 counties." [55] In New Jersey, Puerto Ricans as well as Negroes are slighted in this way. An evaluation of the summer school program revealed that "In 1966, there were close to 100 children at Woodstown who were Spanish-speaking, but there was not one teacher who spoke Spanish. The principal assured us that this wasn't so bad at all, because it forced these children to learn English so as to communicate!" [56]

But "migrants have a 'sub-culture' within that of the poor, including their own non-migrant relatives." [57] It is their transience, their dependence on the season, their absolute lack of roots, which distinguish migrants from other poor people and other nonwhite people. It is misleading, says the migrant ministry, to define a migrant as "one who leaves his home," for the fundamental feature of migrancy is the absence of any concept of "home." [58]

The implications of this rootlessness are vast. The status of the migrant as a "nonresident" and a "noncitizen" have already been considered. Another result is that the housing provided for migrants all along the East Coast is designed to be temporary and strictly for summer use, making it impossible to maintain even the pretense of "home." The situation is especially serious for seasonally employed agricultural workers who live in one place for a long time. A poverty worker in Monmouth County described conditions in Purgolaville: "all but five of the . . . shacks are rented and lack inside toilets, running water and adequate heat . . . [they] are built solely for summer living but many migrant workers live there all year long. I'm trying to determine just how they exist through the winter." [59] The practical effects of movement on human development are best illustrated with reference to an individual case, which deserves to be quoted extensively:

> This infant was first referred to New Jersey by the Delaware State Board of Health in 1965. At that time the child was about 5 months old; it was felt that there was some brain damage, and that there might be need of plastic surgery for the scars present on both temporal areas. The family left Delaware before the child was seen at the E. I. du Pont de Nemours Institute. No definite diagnosis was made.
>
> The child was found and referred to the Family Health Clinic in Salem, New Jersey. The pediatrician felt a neurological work-up was indicated, but the family left New Jersey before the examination could be arranged. Mrs. C. was given a Migrant Health Program stamped, addressed envelope and requested to notify New Jersey when she was located and the health records would be forwarded to the appropriate State. The card was never received.
>
> In July of 1966 Mrs. C. and the now seventeen month old child returned to the Family Clinic in Salem, New Jersey (self referral) and was referred to one of the evaluation clinics participating in the Mental Retardation Program, for a neurological work-up.

A probable diagnosis of Hurler's Syndrome was made and further laboratory tests required.

To date, final reports have not been received on laboratory findings. The family has since moved to Pennsylvania . . .[60]

Adequate followup and continuity of services are aspects of civilized life the migrant simply has to do without.

Even more serious than the way in which migrancy denies the farm workers adequate care are the effects of migrancy itself. The influence of excessive mobility on the individual is only beginning to be examined: "All life is process and, hence, change. From birth to death, no living being can expect to stay in identical circumstances; his body changes, his behavior alters, and his physical and social environments change. We cannot conceive the lack of change. To the extent that change is compatible with existence, absence of change can be identified as stagnation. However, there is a limit of change to which the organism can adapt and still maintain itself as a continuing system." [61] "A number of studies have shown that the process of migration creates mental stresses which, in turn, precipitate mental disorder in susceptible individuals." [62]

For Robert Coles, the subculture of the seasonal agricultural workers is specifically determined "on the basis of their work and travel habits." [63] Coles sees a people characterized by extremes in isolation, in dependence and in insecurity. While demonstrating a number of strengths within their own family and their own community, migrants have tended to be withdrawn, resigned, or at best suspicious with regard to the outside world. "Such alterations in mood and attitude appeared to me as grim and striking examples of the capacity of the human mind to respond to its environment and keep itself intact by developing a high order of ability to divide itself severely and categorically." [64]

This "schizophrenia" of the migrant and the accompanying feelings of helplessness in the face of a hostile world have contributed to the self-perpetuating nature of migrancy. As the U. S. Department of Labor has noted, "It is difficult for the migrant to trade ingrown patterns of survival, however marginal, for unknown ones." [65] Coles himself indicates a number of manifestations of this reliance on ingrown survival patterns. Migrants, for example, are generally fearful of hospitals for maternal care as foreign places where the child will somehow be "hurt," [66] and they avoid eating the foods they pick as something belonging more properly to the outside world. [67]

A report of the State Board of Health of Florida, the closest thing to a home base for New Jersey migrants, has discussed at length the cultural problems involved in migrant health. "Migrants are oriented to the present more so than to the past or future," the study noted. "They do not concern themselves with detailed planning to avert or to cope with critical situations." [68] Thus, "they rarely associate immunizations with preventing diseases," [69] and they "adopt the simplest and most expedient solutions to immediate problems at hand." [70] The attitude of the migrant to health problems was summarized this way: "The health expectations of migrants may be described as being fatalistic in nature. There is an apparent expectation of a certain amount of illness during the course of a year. Such illness is accepted as being normal, not calling for any particular concern or action." [71] It would be difficult to imagine an attitude more at odds with the standards of the American middle class, or one more perfectly geared to maintaining a defeated class.

Another part of the problem is the migrant's own lack of education, and here again one can see the way in which the migrant problem is self-perpetuating. The Florida study found that 74.4 percent of migrant adults were not able to read the word "prenatal" and that 62.7 percent responded incorrectly to the word "pregnant." [72] The New Jersey report confirmed these findings by pointing out that it is essential for services to be brought to the migrant camps rather than to wait for the migrant to seek out services for himself.[73]

It would be a mistake, however, to attribute the migrant's health problems to his own ignorance or to the dictates of his culture. Nor does the primary cause lie in what a California study labeled as "the almost complete nonavailability of medical care." [74] Further, the migrant's "inability to pay for hospitalization and private medical care often restricts or negates potential benefits from clinic service by preventing patient followup or necessary additional medical care in both emergency and rehabilitative situations." [75] At bottom, the problem has to do with the traditional exploitation of the migrant and the conditions under which he lives and works.

The way in which the system depends on human weakness was spotlighted by Truman Moore, who writes of a crew leader who "preferred workers, either male or female, in the first stages of alcoholism." [76] Dale Wright tells of another kind of migrant crew leader: "One Atlantic City sharpie made regular Friday-to-Sunday visits to Bridgeton, with three girls in a closed pickup van. The vehicle was equipped with a folding cot in the back and it could be driven around town from place to place wherever business was best. The price per visit varied from $10 to $20, depending on the [migrant] client's anxiety and the sales ability of the girls." [77] The results of this casual sexual exploitation provide another commentary on the condition of the migrant worker: "In a crew near Morehead City, North Carolina, one woman infected ten men in the course of three days. Six out of eight crews working in the area had at least one syphilitic." [78]

But the worst physical hardships of migrancy have to do with the job itself. Farm work is the third most hazardous industry in the United States,[79] a fact which does not even take into consideration the quality of transportation for farm workers. A 1965 check on migrant vehicles by the Interstate Commerce Commission revealed that "more than half were unsatisfactory from a health standpoint for reasons such as uncleanliness and broken windows."[80] The same results were obtained in a 1963 study of migrant vehicles in New Jersey.[81]

Another part of the problem has been the lack of sanitation facilities on the job. Senator Harrison Williams of New Jersey has pointed out that "Unlike other sectors of our commerce, agriculture generally does not provide migrant farm workers with field-sanitation facilities such as toilets, hand-washing facilities, and potable drinking water."[82] Aside from the obvious dangers to health implicit in this situation, such treatment takes its toll in human dignity: "There were no restrooms in the fields where we worked last season. We went down the row far away where there was nobody working and nobody could see us. The women do not like to work in the fields because of this."[83] Ironically, it may also take its toll in the well-being of the consumer. In our "bath-room-oriented society," writes Truman Moore, "it is not pleasant to imagine that beneath the cellophane wrapper lies a head of lettuce that has been urinated on."[84] But the hazards to the worker are infinitely greater. That the dangers he faces are not limited to mishaps involving farm machinery was shown by a 1958 report in the Journal of the American Medical Association, which revealed that seventy farm workers had been the victims of insecticide poisoning.[85]

But the greatest hazards to health are connected with the living arrangements of the migrant. Almost one-half of the substandard housing found in the United States is located in rural areas, even though less than one-third of the people reside in those areas,[86] much of this housing consists of tar-paper shacks that predominate in New Jersey. It is important to consider the size of the families that inhabit such shacks. The Florida study revealed that although the mean number of persons in a household was 4.2, the mean number of rooms per household was 1.5.[87] The situation among New Jersey Negroes is even worse: shabby barracks that might serve as relatively suitable quarters for male contract workers are simply unlivable for the large Negro families that come North.

The almost complete lack of facilities that accompany this housing—facilities such as garbage and sewerage disposal, heat and potable water—has already been mentioned. The situation was summarized by the writer who observed of the migrant that "the outside world is often his toilet," [88] and perhaps even better by the grower who said, "Oh, heat's no problem. You'd be surprised how hot it gets in one of them little cabins with so many people." [89] But in addition the effect of the absence of adequate cooking facilities, refrigeration and water supplies compounds the already serious dietary problems of the migrant.

The United States Public Health Service reported that among migrants "consumption of certain nutrients was below half the amounts recommended by the Food and Nutrition Board of the National Research Council." [90] The report showed that the families under study "had diagnoses of rickets, marasmas, kwarshiorkor, obesity, emaciation, nutritional anemia, and malnutrition . . . many of the children in the families with lower intakes of nutrients were pale and underweight, and eight adults were markedly obese." [91] And these findings do not even reflect the gravity of the situation, since they are based on "apparently well" families only.[92]

The conditions under which the migrant lives—the exploitation, the indifference or hostility of the community, the lack of services, the "slop jar," the twice-a-day meals, the fear and the withdrawal—all these have led to a health situation which would turn the stomach of the middle-class consumer if he ever let himself dwell on it. It is simply impossible to live under circumstances which provide a haven for rodents and insects, and to exist on a diet consisting of nothing better than pig's feet and soft drinks and hope to enjoy anything resembling a normal way of life. The most depressing aspect of the problem, as the Public Health Service has pointed out, is that "there is no effective way to quarantine the results of poor housing within the particular area where the housing exists," [93] and the same is true of the other sectors of migrant life.

All available literature on the subject of migrant health has emphasized that migrants suffer to a staggering degree from the entire range of physical problems. One summary pointed out that migrants "are more prone than others to such illnesses as pinworms, diarrhea, contagious skin infections, acute febrile tonsillitis, lymph-adenopathy, asthma, iron-deficiency anemia, scurvy, rickets, and disabling physical handicaps such as dental abnormalities, and deafness." [94] Another study has emphasized "uncorrected disturbances of vision . . . [and] valvular heart diseases, congenital and rheumatic, that are associated with impaired circulation of the blood," as well as "untreated or poorly treated, chronic and recurrent, veneral diseases . . . chronic kidney and bladder infections . . . muscle pains and bruises or bone injuries or back diseases brought on by working conditions . . . [and] nerve palsies." [95]

Indicative of the migrant health situation are dental problems (one study revealed that 84 percent of the persons examined had dental cavities and 35 percent had lost permanent teeth)[96] and diarrhea (which is so common that it "is not clearly recognized by the family as a threat to health").[97] Both problems are unavoidable corollaries to the migrant's way of life, particularly his poor diet. The New Jersey Department of Health lists them among the five chief problems among migrants in the state; the others are intestinal parasites, eye disease and the somewhat understated problem of tuberculosis.[98]

But the most serious of the migrant health problems, particularly with reference to retardation, are disorders of the genitourinary system. According to the Florida study, such disorders occur in from 10 to 20 percent of the migrant population.[99] While venereal disease, especially syphilis, is a major problem, the greatest problem is in the area of prenatal care. The study showed low hemoglobin and extremes of blood pressure to be prevalent among pregnant women; in combination with the problem of frequent pregnancies, lack of adequate prenatal care and insufficient funds for private medical care,[100] the Florida survey provided a good indication of the reasons for the high incidence of birth disorders among New Jersey migrants. It is worth noting that of the ten families studied by Coles in only two were the children delivered by doctors.[101]

At least four relevant observations concerning these health conditions should be noted. The first is that they are far more severe than those experienced by the general population;[102] the infant mortality rate, for example, is three times that found in urban areas.[103] The second is that these problems do not merely constitute annoyances for the migrant; rather, they are responsible for "causing a great deal of disability, significant mortality, associated economic loss and other problems." [104] Third, beyond the aggravation of the migrants' economic difficulties through illness, it must be recognized that "such illnesses cannot help but affect the minds of people regularly suffering from not one but in all likelihood many of them." [105] And fourth, in order to appreciate the damage to the human mind of which migrancy is capable, it is necessary to consider that about one-third of the people in the migrant stream are children:[106] "between a quarter and a half million children under 18 are caught in this kind of living." [107]

All of the hazards of migrant life are intensified when experienced by children. Truman Moore reports that in California over five hundred farm workers, eighteen years old or under, receive serious injuries every year.[108] The situation is typified by a 2½-year-old Illinois migrant boy who died after drinking from a jar that still contained a little of the milky liquid used to spray cabbages.[109] Perhaps even more tragic and more common is the case of another 2½-year-old who "looked only 12 months old because he was so undernourished." [110] A report on day care published by the Department of Health, Education and Welfare indicated that the health, nutrition and general living problems of migrant children are immense: "Malnourishment is frequent. The level of immunization is distressingly low, in some surveys up to 100 percent incomplete. Rarely more than half of the children received immunization against poliomyelitis; about one-third of the children have been vaccinated. Diarrhea is prevalent, and among infants is the most common cause of disease and death." [111] The report also indicated that "of 65 children surveyed in a middle-western State, 15 were found with previously unknown or inadequately cared for health problems." [112] In another report, the United States Children's Bureau emphasized the relationship between these health problems and the lack of child care and child welfare services and facilities.[113]

The influence of these physical deprivations on the well-being of the migrant child cannot be underestimated. As the New Jersey Department of Education put it, "children who suffer from empty stomachs, weariness, toothaches, painful cuts, insect bites, vision and hearing defects, are not likely to grow strong and learn well." [114] The case of one child in a New Jersey school illustrated the problem of malnourishment: "Retardation in social and mental development could be attributed, at least partially, to constant malnourishment through infancy and the preschool years. Now at six, puny, uncoordinated, nonverbal, he was the scapegoat of the older boys in whose laughter-less lives his performances provided perverted forms of entertainment." [115] Summarizing the findings of many states, the Children's Bureau provided a clear indication of the sort of hardships faced by the migrant child: "Some [children] are chronically sleepy and irritable because they do not sleep well in noisy, crowded camps. Some suffer from the competition and conflict of family life. Older children need help to bear and to understand the differences in their living conditions from other children's." [116]

Such conditions go far toward explaining the almost unbelievable degree of retardation among these "children of harvest." The statistics of this retardation deserve careful attention:

> Over one-third of the children became retarded as early as their second year in school. Percentages of retardation mounted steadily. For children with 9 years of schooling 75 per cent were retarded. After the fourth year in school well over half the children were retarded from two to five years. Two-thirds of the children were over-age for the grade. In the 11-12 year age group two years over-age was the median; in the 13-16 year age group it was three years. More than one-third of the group reporting normal age-grade status were 6-7 year-olds who had not been in school long enough to become retarded in age-grade relationships.

> Added to these direct evidences of retardation were the judgments expressed by teachers concerning scholastic achievement. These indicated that in grades 2 to 6, between one-third and one-half were placed from one to three grades higher than their scholastic attainment warranted. [117]

Other studies have shown even higher levels of retardation. One reported that "the percentage of retardation rises rapidly after the age of nine and comprises 87 percent of the 15-year-old-group." [118] Another found that "above the tenth birthday, retardation appeared in from 95 percent to 99 percent of the cases, with the median extent of retardation ranging between three and four years." [119] The United States Office of Education summarized these findings this way: "The migrant children have the lowest educational attainments of any group in the Nation. They enter school later, attend fewer days, show greatest retardation, achieve the least progress, drop out of school earliest, and constitute the largest single reservoir of illiterates." [120]

It would be wrong, however, to attribute this situation chiefly to organically based mental retardation. A Wisconsin report was probably correct in contending that "the group of children with whom we worked were retarded only in the educational sense." [121] If this is so, the figures on retardation among migrants indicate a tremendous waste of human potential. For those migrants who have survived the physical obstacles to development, retardation must be ascribed to the economic and working conditions of the migrants, the cultural pattern into which he has been forced, and the failure of the educational establishment.

Perhaps the greatest factor blocking the educational achievement of the migrant child is that there is a "direct competition between the economic needs of the family . . . and the educational needs of the children." [122] Not the least of the ironies of migrant life is the fact that, on the one hand, "workers with children often find the economic compulsion to migrate particularly strong," while, on the other, "still further evidence of the importance of the economic incentive is found in the frequent, and sometimes illegal, employment of migrant children in the fields." [123] This situation is reflected in the fact that by far the leading reason for nonenrollment of migrant children in New Jersey migrant summer schools is "working in agriculture." A strong second is "arrived too late or too recently," which also has much to do with the migrant life, as do several of the other reasons: "sickness or physical handicap," "caring for younger children," "rejected by the school," and "no clothes." [124] In a study done by Shirley E. Greene, it was found that only 78 percent of the children in the seven-to-fifteen-year age bracket were enrolled in school.[125] This compared with an enrollment in the general population of 95.7 percent for the seven-to-thirteen group, and 92.9 percent for the fourteen-to-fifteen group.[126]

Enrollment figures for the New Jersey summer schools, at 80 percent, resemble those elsewhere, but "caution," notes the evaluator, "should be observed." He reports: "Firstly, these figures do *not* take into account those children who registered for school but *who never attended:* One wonders what happened to them and what efforts were made to find out why they were not attending. Secondly, in some cases, when students have not attended for many consecutive days, they are dropped from the school roll." [127] It should be added that these figures also fail to account for children who were never recruited. In a state where the earnings of most families are so low that it is in the interest of the family as well as of the grower to keep the child working, in a state where the labor laws permit the summertime employment of children in agriculture after the age of twelve, and where enforcement of even these laws is almost nonexistent, and in a state where followup recruitment by school officials is less than dynamic, it is easy to see that many children simply were left out. These are the "kids that don't count."

The practical obstacles to attendance, nationally as well as in New Jersey, were summarized by two actions of Congress in 1966. A proposal by Senator Harrison Williams to restrict the use of child labor on farms was removed from a minimum wage bill by the Senate Labor Committee.[128] And the bill itself fixed the agricultural minimum at only one dollar an hour for 1967, to be raised to only $1.30 by 1969.[129] The present New Jersey farm minimum is higher, at $1.25, but since it includes an allowance to the grower for the "housing" he provides, it may actually lower present wage levels. At the same time, a proposal to give migrant families a modest stipend for each child in school has not been approved, thus assuring that attendance will remain low.

In addition to economic considerations, the constant movement of the migrant child jeopardizes his educational opportunities.[130] Greene reports that the degree of family mobility determines the degree of schooling received. Further, "78.9 pecent had maintained no continuous residence as long as 30 weeks during the preceding year. Yet 62.0 percent of the children reported attendance at only one school." [131] When these children do attend additional schools, they face the kind of paradoxical situation as that noted by the New Jersey evaluator: "In some cases, these youngsters . . . are older than the local children, and certain serious psychological problems which impede learning are created. Where school authorities try to avoid this problem by placing the migrant children among their age-peers, they create a situation where these youngsters are so far out of step with the other children in the room that a different complex of psychological difficulties, equally harmful to learning, is created." [132] It is not surprising, in view of such situations, that "migrancy has an adverse effect on the child's normal progress through school, upon his development of basic operational intelligence, upon his achievement in the basic skills in reading and arithmetic and upon personality growth and emotional adjustment." [133] Nor is it surprising that migrant children in school tend to be frustrated, lonely and withdrawn in the classroom.[134]

But such feelings have less to do with the classroom situation than with the migrant child's very way of life. Mobility seems to have an even more profound effect on the child than on the adult: "With respect to residential mobility, in illustration, a short distance move may imply a complete change in environment for the child, due to the fact that he cannot get around by himself, although there is virtually little or no change involved for the parents. . . . Families who changed residence reported a higher initial level of disturbance in the child than families who did not change residence."[135] At the same time, however, migrant children receive none of the benefits that one would expect from travel. "Families do not stop to view natural scenic beauty and places of historical interest, except in an incidental way."[136] For migrant children, "Their world was circumscribed by crops to pick, bags and boxes and hampers to lift, mean ill-smelling shanties to live in and the landlord to be paid his money at the end of the week. . . . it was a futile existence, from which escape was possible but extremely difficult."[137]

Migrant children are also handicapped in that they lack wholesome surroundings at home: "The families live in conditions which permit the most meager social and recreational possibilities. Their children lack stimulation and opportunity to learn basic skills which would ready them for school. The babies obviously are frequently deprived of warm, personal handling by responsible adults. They may not be touched or spoken to for hour after hour."[138] In addition, notes Coles, there is almost no printed matter in the migrants' homes.[139] What migrant children do bring to bear on the school situation is an entirely different kind of background: "Even as six-year-olds, they may hear family dis-

cussions of unemployment, desertion, and adultery. They
have seen much of drinking, quarreling, infidelity, encounters with the law, sickness and death." [140] The chief obstacles to migrant learning, writes Greene, are physical illness, broken homes, illegitimacy and the educational limits
of parents.[141] Greene demonstrates that there is a close
correlation between the educational level of the parents and
the degree to which they are entrenched in the agricultural
life, on the one hand, and the educational achievement of
the child,[142] on the other.

The disorganization of the migrant family surpasses that
for almost any other group in society. The Florida study, for
example, agrees with the finding that "slightly over one-half
(53.4%) of all of the households were classified as unstable." [143] In addition, many migrant households have female heads,[144] a factor which, as has been shown, may
have an adverse effect on educational performance.[145] Beyond this observation, it should be recognized that the
whole approach of the migrant to family life is informal by
middle-class standards. "The current husband is almost always called 'father' by all children," writes Coles, "and his
name is assumed." [146] The family life of the migrant is a
basic part of the "uprootedness" which "is a constant fact of
life from birth to death." [147] One of Coles's most important
findings is his examination of the drawings of migrant children. "One little boy of seven emphasized his own kind of
living (its rootlessness) by spending considerable time on
the kind of foundation (including an elaborate cellar) he
gave to the houses he imagined non-migrants to have." [148]

Of even greater significance to the migrant child is the
fact that his life pattern is determined by his biological development. The beginning of his adulthood is marked by the
experience of working in the field and by the advent of pu-
berty.[149] School for migrant children loses out to employment, not only for financial reasons, but also because the

way of life forced on farm workers makes it impossible for the young migrant even to regard himself as a child. Having come directly from a childhood devoted to "confirming the child's sense of submission to the non-migrant world, or passivity before it," [150] directly into a too early adulthood, the young migrant simply has no opportunity to undergo a normal educational development.

These disadvantages of migrant life, however, are only a part of the story. The other part is that while "many of these rural children are sick in body [and] uneducated in mind," they are "quite strong and effective psychologically, so long as their strength and capacity to manage their lives are judged by the standards—the obligations and challenges— of their own world." [151] It is precisely this way of viewing the migrant that the educational establishment has been unwilling to adopt. And this, says Coles, is the "tragedy of inner strength"—the "tenacious and willful people who are the migrants are unable to find any fulfillment in an educational system which lacks all meaning for their kind of life." [152] "The school building Ruth finally managed to draw was distinctly small, dwarfed by a giant pine tree and off to one side of the paper . . . She used a black crayon, and supplied no windows or doors. In fact it was an isolated box, essentially irrelevant to the carefully drawn landscape." [153] The fundamental problem of migrant education is that there is no "sensible connection" between what happens in the school and what happens in the migrants' lives.[154]

Certainly this sort of connection has been missing from the New Jersey summer educational program. In one school, children were made to learn a mindless jingle—almost a taunt—which ended with these lines: "From Cape May to Sussex no further will I roam, New Jersey, New Jersey, the Garden State my home." [155] And yet at the same school a perfect illustration of the isolation of these children was discovered by the evaluator: "All the books and materials used by the children in 'regular' school were locked away in closets or sealed from use with long strips of wrapping paper completely across the shelves . . . Furthermore, school libraries were, in a number of cases, not utilized; in some cases they were *forbidden* to be used." [156] The program is not entirely without books, however; "Through a kind book salesman," wrote the program director in 1956, "several discarded books were given us." [157] Aside from this there was almost no educational material in any of the seven schools, with the exception of the school at Englishtown.[158]

Even more important, the program missed an opportunity to fill the vacuum of educational material in the migrant's home, and on the road,[159] a step that would do much to provide a meaningful link between the school and the camp. In addition, the schools did almost nothing in the way of including the parents in the school program.[160] The Department of Education held out against attempts of the Office of Economic Opportunity to have migrant mothers hired as subprofessional aides in the schools, a procedure that would have helped to remove from the schools the stigma of being an alien place. One principal—a mother herself—when asked if she would accept the aide idea, replied, "Perhaps if I need someone to sweep the floor." [161]

The schools were able to use the federal money set aside for employment of migrant aides to hire the daughter of one of the richest growers in the state and the daughter of the president of one of the local boards of education.[162] The Department of Education was proud of the experience it provided for these college students: "It should pay rich dividends when they become full fledged teachers." [163]

The Department was also proud of its "much discussed innovation—the non-graded school" and of its curriculum, which "started where he [the child] was and developed from there." [164] It appears likely, however, that these "innovations" were the result of confusion within the migrant program. Although the program was specifically designed, both by the Department of Education and by the Office of Economic Opportunity, to be remedial in nature,[165] the fact is that *"There is no curriculum. There is no formal curriculum. There is no informal curriculum."* [166] Despite the clarity of the guidelines with regard to remediation, the program director was quoted as saying, "We don't conceive of this program as being remedial in nature." [167] The principals echoed this with, "We do not have an academically oriented program. . . . our primary concern is not to have an academic program." [168] And one of the teachers said: "I've *never* heard of this before . . . and I've been in this program for five years. No one ever told us that." [169]

There seems to be much else that the schools never heard of. Not only is record transferral to other states almost nonexistent, "in most schools there are no such records at all." [170] Nor is there any attempt to use the kind of specialists migrant children need,[171] or to go outside the local community for skilled teachers.[172] Further, a meaningful teacher-training program was entirely absent: "No one seemed to have any clear notion of what was actually said there; a few felt it was 'nice'; others thought that the main value was 'in getting to meet State Department people; you don't often get a chance like that.' " [173]

The primary emphasis of the summer school program seemed to aim at providing the children with a pleasant temporary alternative to working in the fields. "We try to make it nice for these kids," said one teacher, "but there's not much you can do for them. In a few years they'll just be out there picking crops." The principal at the same school, who described himself as a friend of the grower, specifically denied that the purpose of the program was to help migrant children to leave the migrant stream.[174] The self-fulfilling prophecy has never been more accurate than with regard to the migratory farm worker.

It has been written of New Jersey migrants that "Their most realistic hope is to finish the Florida season with enough money to make the trip up North, and to finish the Northern season with enough money to make the trip back South." [175] But it is impossible to understand the migrant life unless one realizes that the same sort of hopeless cycle operates from generation to generation. "The end product [of migrant childhood and migrant education]," concludes the Office of Education, "is a citizen who has no social or geographic roots, has a feeling of being left out, is ill-prepared for any form of constructive citizenship, and lacks the basic educational tools for satisfactory living." [176] Or, as it has also been stated, the background of the migrant makes him "a misfit and an isolate wherever he goes." [177]

If the migrant is isolated from the rest of society, it is largely because the rest of society prefers to isolate itself from the migrant and has seen to it that the migrant is at a comfortable distance from itself. "We want to 'forget' what amounts in sum to a vastly unpleasant and complicated state of affairs," [178] says Coles. Until there is a real effort to bridge the gap between the two cultures—"ours" and "theirs"—it will be as true of the middle-class American on his interstate highway as it is of the migrant in his moveable ghetto to say that all his mobility has gotten him nowhere. "Always on the way. Always goin' and goin'," wrote John Steinbeck. "Seems to me we don't never come to nothin'." [179]

Notes

Chapter I: A New Assessment

1. Louis Pizzo, quoted by Ronald Sullivan, "Jersey Farmers Bar Vista Group," *The New York Times* (September 2, 1966).

2. B. H. Bradley, rev. of "Public Impressions of the Mentally Retarded," *Mental Retardation Abstracts,* I (1964), p. 47.

3. G. E. Milligan, rev. of Murray, J., "Responses of College Men and Women to a Test on Knowledge of Mental Deficiency," *Mental Retardation Abstracts,* I (1964), p. 46.

4. "National Action to Combat Mental Retardation," *President's Panel on Mental Retardation* (October, 1962), p. 8.

5. *Miles to Go* (Connecticut Mental Retardation Project Report, March, 1966), p. 127.

6. "National Action to Combat Mental Retardation," p. 10.

7. Patricia C. Sexton, *Education and Income* (New York, 1961), p. 16.

8. Sexton, p. 18.

9. Douglas W. Bray, *Issues in the Study of Talent* (New York, 1954), p. 15.

10. Henry H. Goddard, *The Kallikak Family, A Study in the Heredity of Feeblemindedness* (New York, 1912).

11. Seymour B. Sarason, Thomas Gladwin, and Richard L. Masland, *Mental Subnormality* (New York, 1958), p. 196.

12. I. Goldstein, "Implications of Mental Deficiency," *Occupational Education,* V (1948), p. 152.

13. R. C. Scheerenberger, "Genetic Aspects of Mental Retardation," *Mental Retardation Abstracts,* II, No. 4 (October–December, 1965), p. 463.

14. R. C. Scheerenberger, et al., p. 463.

15. Donald Janson, "Is Health Care a Right or a Privilege?" *The New York Times* (July 2, 1967), p. 8E.

16. Mel Ravitz, "The Role of the School in the Urban Setting," *Education in Depressed Areas,* ed. A. Harry Passow (New York, 1963), p. 19.

17. Lee Rainwater, "Crucible of Identity: The Negro Lower-Class Family," *Daedalus* (Winter, 1966), p. 209.

18. Author's analysis of Median IQ scores, Newark Department of Education, 1964.

19. George Tarjan, "Prevention—A Program Goal in Mental Deficiency," *Mental Retardation,* ed. Jerome H. Rothstein (New York, 1961), p. 135.

20. Herschel W. Nisonger, *Guidelines for Comprehensive State Planning in Mental Retardation,* American Association on Mental Deficiency (September 15, 1964), p. 9.

21. Sarason, et al., p. 145.

22. Georges Sabagh, Harvey F. Dingman, George Tarjan, and Stanley W. Wright, "Social Class and Ethnic Status of Patients Admitted to a State Hospital for the Retarded," *Pacific Sociological Review,* II, No. 2 (Fall, 1959), p. 80.

23. Tarjan, "Prevention—A Program Goal in Mental Deficiency," p. 125.

24. Personal communication by author with members of the Division of Special Education, New Jersey Department of Education, March, 1967.

25. Christine P. Ingram, *Education of the Slow Learning Child,* 2nd ed. (New York, 1953), p. 4.

26. George A. Jervis, "Medical Aspects of Mental Deficiency," *American Journal of Mental Deficiency,* V (October, 1941), p. 216.

27. Edgar A. Doll, "The Essentials of an Inclusive Concept of Mental Deficiency," *American Journal of Mental Deficiency,* VI (October, 1941), p. 216.

28. Seymour Sarason, *Psychology of Exceptional Children,* ed. W. W. Cruickshank (New York, 1955), pp. 440–442.

29. Rick Heber, *A Manual on Terminology and Classification in Mental Retardation,* American Association on Mental Deficiency (1961), p. 3.

30. John Martin, director, Office of Technical Assistance, New Jersey Office of Economic Opportunity, personal communication, July, 1967.

31. Vernon F. Haubrich, "Teachers for Big-City Schools," *Education in Depressed Areas,* ed. A. Harry Passow (New York, 1963), p. 243, note 2.

32. Martin.

33. Helen E. Martz, "National Blueprint for Public Welfare," *Health, Education and Welfare Indicators* (Washington: U. S. Government Printing Office, 1966), p. 10.

34. *Juvenile Delinquency and Youth Crime,* Task Force on Juvenile Delinquency (Washington: U. S. Government Printing Office, 1967), p. 55.

35. Lola M. Irelan and Arthur Besner, "Low-Income Outlook on Life," *Low-Income Life Styles,* ed. L. M. Irelan (Washington: U. S. Government Printing Office, 1966), p. 2.

36. Ben H. Bagdikian, *In the Midst of Plenty* (New York, 1964), p. 57.

37. Oscar Lewis, "The Culture of Poverty," *Scientific American,* CCXV, No. 4 (October, 1966), p. 21.

38. "36% of Nonwhites in the U. S. Earned Under $3,000 in '66," *The New York Times* (August 11, 1967).

39. James Weldon Johnson, *The Autobiography of an Ex-Coloured Man* (Boston, 1927), p. 21.

40. J. H. Griffin, *Black Like Me* (Boston, 1961), p. 53.

41. John Steinbeck, *The Grapes of Wrath* (New York, 1939), p. 280.

42. Lewis, pp. 19–20.

43. Alfred Binet, *Les Idées Modernes sur les Enfants* (Paris, 1909), pp. 54–55, quoted by J. McV. Hunt, *Intelligence and Experience* (New York, 1961), p. 13.

44. G. D. Stoddard, *The Meaning of Intelligence* (New York, 1943), p. 281.

45. Thomas F. Pettigrew, *A Profile of the Negro American* (Princeton, New Jersey, 1964), p. 108.

46. C. Burt, E. Jones, E. Miller, and W. Moodie, *How the Mind Works* (New York, 1934), p. 28.

47. J. H. Rohrer, "The Test Intelligence of Osage Indians," *Journal of Social Psychology,* XVI (1942), pp. 99–105.

48. W. S. Neff, "Socio-economic Status and Intelligence: A Critical Survey," *Psychological Bulletin,* XXXV (1938), p. 754.

49. O. Klineberg, *Negro Intelligence and Selective Migration* (New York, 1935).

50. Harold M. Skeels and Marie Skodak, *Adult Status of*

Individuals Who Experienced Early Intervention, American Association on Mental Deficiency (May 12, 1966), pp. 6–7. The authors reported on the 1939 study in this monograph.

51. H. Carl Haywood and Jack T. Tapp, "Experience and the Development of Adaptive Behavior," *International Review of Research in Mental Retardation,* ed. N. R. Ellis, I (New York, 1966), p. 33 (in galley proof).

52. Haywood and Tapp, p. 33.

53. Haywood and Tapp, p. 34.

54. Haywood and Tapp, p. 35.

55. Richard Kobler and Robert Weber, *The Crisis in Human Underdevelopment,* Responsive Environment Corporation (March, 1967), pp. 19–20.

56. Kobler and Weber, p. 20.

57. H. Carl Haywood, *Experimental Factors in Intellectual Development: The Concept of Dynamic Intelligence,* American Psychological Association (February, 1966), p. 17.

58. Allison Davis and Kenneth Eells, *Davis-Eells Test of General Intelligence or Problem-Solving Ability* (New York, 1958), pp. 6–7.

59. Davis and Eells, p. 7.

60. Sarason, et al., *Mental Subnormality,* pp. 159–160.

61. Editorial, "The I. Q. Meter," *New Republic* (September, 1960), p. 6.

62. Allison Davis, *Social-Class Influences Upon Learning* (Cambridge, Mass., 1948), as quoted in *The Culturally Deprived Child,* Frank Riessman (New York, 1962), p. 52.

63. A. Anastasi and F. A. Cordova, "Some Effects of Bi-Lingualism Upon the Intelligence Test Performance of Puerto Rican Children in New York City," *Journal of Educational Psychology,* XLIV (1953), p. 6.

64. Frank Riessman, *The Culturally Deprived Child* (New York, 1962), pp. 49–66.

65. Haggard, pp. 141–186.

66. Martin Deutsch, "The Disadvantaged Child and the Learning Process," *Education in Depressed Areas,* ed. A. Harry Passow (New York, 1963), p. 172.

67. Riessman, p. 53.

68. Allison Davis, "Socio-economic Influences Upon Children's Learning," speech delivered at the mid-century White

House Conference on Children and Youth (December 5, 1960).

69. Heber, p. 64.

70. Heber, p. 41.

71. Heber, p. 65.

72. Heber, p. 65.

73. Rainwater, p. 206.

74. *Juvenile Delinquency and Youth Crime,* p. 43.

75. Kenneth B. Clark, *Dark Ghetto* (New York, 1965), pp. 89–90.

76. Clark, p. 13.

77. "High Prices Found in Poor Areas," *The New York Times* (July 24, 1967), p. 29.

78. Robert B. Semple, Jr., "Wirtz Finds Lag in Hiring Negroes," *The New York Times* (May 5, 1967).

79. Michael Harrington, *The Other America* (Baltimore, 1962), p. 138.

80. Harvey F. Dingman and George Tarjan, "Mental Retardation and the Normal Distribution Curve," *American Journal of Mental Deficiency,* LXIV, No. 6 (May, 1960), p. 991.

81. A. D. B. Clarke, "The Measurement of Intelligence: Its Validity and Reliability," *Mental Deficiency, the Changing Outlook,* eds. Ann M. Clarke and A. D. B. Clarke (Glencoe, Ill., 1958), p. 69.

82. Dingman and Tarjan, p. 991.

83. P. U. Lemkau, "Epidemiological Aspects," *The Evaluation and Treatment of the Mentally Retarded Child in Clinics* (New York, 1956).

84. "National Action to Combat Mental Retardation," p. 1.

85. *The Problem of Mental Retardation* (Washington: U. S. Government Printing Office, 1966), p. 16.

86. *The Underdeveloped Resource: A Plan for the Mentally Retarded in California* (California Study Commission on Mental Retardation, January, 1965), p. 18.

87. *The New Jersey Comprehensive Plan to Combat Mental Retardation* (New Jersey Division of Mental Retardation, June, 1966), p. 51.

88. Will Lissner, "Negro Called Victim of Technology Era," *The New York Times* (July 28, 1967), p. 10.

89. Ann E. Dickerson, "Mental Retardation in the Negro Community: The Influence of Social Economic Factors," The

Centennial Conference on the Health Status of the Negro Today and in the Future, Howard University, Washington, D. C. (March 13–14, 1967), p. 33.

90. *Miles to Go,* p. 118.

91. Lyndon B. Johnson, quoted in *The Problems of Mental Retardation,* p. 19.

92. Cited in *The New Jersey Comprehensive Plan to Combat Mental Retardation,* p. 52.

93. Burton Blatt, "Some Persistently Recurring Assumptions Concerning the Mentally Subnormal," *Mental Retardation,* ed. J. H. Rothstein, p. 118.

94. Joseph F. Jastak, Halsey M. MacPhee, and Martin Whiteman, *Mental Retardation: Its Nature and Incidence,* Delaware (New York, 1963).

Onondaga County Survey: A Special Census of Suspected-Referred Mental Retardation (New York State Department of Mental Hygiene, 1955).

See the "Biennial Report of the Eugenics Board of North Carolina," for July 1, 1962 to June 30, 1964 and for July 1, 1964 to June 30, 1966. Hereafter cited as "Biennial Report."

Mental Retardation in Arkansas (Mental Retardation Planning Project, Arkansas State Department of Health, 1966).

Maurice G. Kott, "Estimating the Number of the Retarded in New Jersey," *Estimating Rehabilitation Needs,* ed. Monroe Berkowitz (New Brunswick, New Jersey, 1967).

Robert L. Erdman and James L. Olson, "Relationships Between Emotional Programs for the Mentally Retarded and the Culturally Deprived," *Mental Retardation Abstracts,* III, No. 3 (July–September, 1966).

R. J. Havighurst, "The Public Schools of Chicago" (Chicago Board of Education, 1964).

J. A. Lane, rev. of Robert A. Wakefield, "An Investigation of the Family Background of Educable Mentally Retarded Children in Special Classes," *Exceptional Children,* XXXI, No. 3 (1964), in *Mental Retardation Abstracts,* II, No. 2 (April–June, 1965).

95. L. M. Dunn, "Educable Mentally Retarded Children," *Exceptional Children in the Schools,* ed. L. M. Dunn (New York, 1963), quoted by Haywood and Tapp, p. 35.

96. "The Problem of Mental Retardation," p. 1.

97. "Biennial Report," 1964–1966, p. 31.

98. "Biennial Report," 1964–1966, p. 26.
99. "Biennial Report," 1964–1966, p. 31.
100. "Biennial Report," 1964–1966, p. 9.
101. "Biennial Report," 1964–1966, p. 9.
102. *United States Bureau of the Census, Census of Population* (Washington: U. S. Government Printing Office, 1960).
103. "Biennial Report," 1964–1966, p. 9.
104. "Biennial Report," 1964–1966, p. 7
105. "Biennial Report," 1964–1966, p. 7.
106. "Biennial Report," p. 9.
107. "Biennial Report," p. 9.
108. "Rank Correlation Coefficient Comparing Rank Order of Special Class Norms, Selected School Districts, Compared to Rank of Other Social and Economic Variables in the Selected Districts for the Year 1960," (unpublished data) Implementation Project, New Jersey Division of Mental Retardation, 1966.
109. Sarason, et al., *Mental Subnormality,* p. 306.
110. Child, quoted by Walter E. Schafer and Kenneth Polk, "Delinquency and the Schools," *Juvenile Delinquency and Youth Crime,* p. 241.
111. D. Gibson and A. J. Butler, "Culture as a Possible Contributor to Feeblemindedness," *American Journal of Mental Deficiency,* LVIII, No. 3 (January, 1954), pp. 490–495, in Sarason, et al., *Mental Subnormality,* p. 239.
112. A. M. Shotwell, "Arthur Performance Ratings of Mexican and American High-Grade Mental Defectives," *American Journal of Mental Deficiency,* XLIX (1945), pp. 445–559, in Sarason, et al., *Mental Subnormality,* p. 240.
113. Robert B. Edgerton, "A Patient Elite: Ethnography in a Hospital for the Mentally Retarded," *American Journal of Mental Deficiency,* LXVIII, No. 3 (November, 1963), pp. 372–385.
114. Edgerton, p. 384.
115. J. Jastak and M. Whiteman, "The Prevalence of Mental Retardation in Delaware: Preliminary Report on a State-Wide Survey," *The Nature and Transmission of the Genetic and Cultural Characteristics of Human Populations* (New York, 1957), pp. 66–67.

Chapter II: Poverty and Organic Impairment

1. Hilda Knobloch and Benjamin Pasamanick, "Distribution of Intellectual Potential in an Infant Population," *Epidemiology of Mental Disorders,* ed. B. Pasamanick, Publ. No. 60, American Association for the Advancement of Science (Washington, 1959), p. 269.

2. Knobloch and Pasamanick, p. 250.

3. Knobloch and Pasamanick, pp. 261–262.

4. Richard L. Masland, Seymour B. Sarason, and Thomas Gladwin, *Mental Subnormality* (New York, 1958), p. 64.

5. Alan F. Guttmacher, *Babies by Choice or by Chance* (New York, 1961), pp. 122–180.

6. Howard J. Osofsky, John H. Hagen, Bernard B. Braen, Peggy W. Wood, and Robert DiFlorio, "Problems of the Pregnant Schoolgirl—An Attempted Solution" (draft of interim report), pp. 1–4, *passim.*

7. Rowland V. Rider, Matthew Taback, and Hilda Knobloch, "Associations between Premature Birth and Socio-economic Status," *American Journal of Public Health,* XLV (1955), pp. 1022–1028, *passim.*

8. Masland, et. al., pp. 64–65.

9. Burdett Wylie, "The Challenge of Infant Mortality," *Bulletin,* Cleveland Academy of Medicine (June, 1965), quoted in *The Health Status of the Negro Today and in the Future* (Washington, D. C., 1967), p. 11. See also Robert A. Aldrich, "Liquidation of the Problem through Research and Training," in *Proceedings, The White House Conference on Mental Retardation* (Washington: U. S. Government Printing Office, 1963), p. 82. Dr. Aldrich calculates that at least 22 percent of all premature infants who survive will be so mentally retarded as to require institutional care. Since, among the nation's population as a whole, the rate of incidence for this group (requiring institutional care) is at most .3 percent, Dr. Wylie's estimate seems quite conservative, especially since these persons who require institutional care make up no more than 10 percent of all retarded persons.

10. Ronald Freedman, Lolagene C. Coombs, and Judith Friedman, "Social Correlates of Fetal Mortality," *The Millbank Memorial Fund Quarterly,* XLIV (July, 1966), pp. 328–329.

11. Masland, et al., p. 102.

12. Eleanor P. Hunt and Earl E. Huyck, "Mortality of White and Nonwhite Infants in Major U. S. Cities," *Health, Education and Welfare Trends,* 1965 Edition, Part 2, *State Data and State Rankings* (Washington: U. S. Government Printing Office), p. 13.

13. Hunt and Huyck, p. 15.

14. Masland, et al., p. 102.

15. Janet B. Hardy, "Perinatal Factors and Intelligence," *The Biosocial Basis of Mental Retardation,* eds. Sonia F. Osler and Robert E. Cooke (Baltimore, 1965), p. 50.

16. Mark Abramowicz and Edward H. Kass, "Pathogenesis and Prognosis of Prematurity," p. 1. Reprint by U. S. Children's Bureau of original series in *New England Journal of Medicine* (October 20, 27, and November 3, 10, 1966).

17. Freedman, et al., p. 4.

18. Freedman, et al., p. 4.

19. Freedman, et al., p. 4.

20. Rider, et al., p. 1025.

21. Abramowicz and Kass, p. 3.

22. Abramowicz and Kass, p. 3.

23. Hunt and Huyck, p. 14.

24. Hunt and Huyck, p. 13.

25. Shirley A. Mayer, "Maternal and Infant Care Project in Newark; A Progress Report," *Public Health News,* XLVIII.

26. Hunt and Huyck, p. 2.

27. Fred J. Cook, *The Plot Against the Patient* (Englewood Cliffs, New Jersey, 1967), p. 27. The corrected rate for Sweden for 1965 is from *Pocket Data Book: USA, 1967* (Washington: U. S. Government Printing Office, 1966), p. 56.

28. Hunt and Huyck, p. 2.

29. Philip S. Lawrence, et al., *Medical Care, Health Status, and Family Income* (Washington: U. S. Government Printing Office, 1964), p. 3.

30. Mayer, p. 107.

31. Abramowicz and Kass, p. 2.

32. Wylie, as noted.

33. Hunt and Huyck, p. 2.

34. Mayer, p. 110.

35. Abramowicz and Kass, p. 3.

36. Hardy, pp. 51–52.

37. *A Proposed Program for National Action to Combat*

Mental Retardation (Washington: U. S. Government Printing Office, 1962), p. 51. Hereafter referred to as *Proposed.*
38. *Proposed,* p. 51.
39. *Proposed,* p. 51.
40. *Proposed,* p. 51.
41. *Proposed,* p. 52.
42. Lawrence, et al., p. 30.
43. Hunt and Huyck, p. 13.
44. John D. Thompson, "The Quality of Human Reproduction," in *Proceedings, The White House Conference on Mental Retardation* (Washington: U. S. Government Printing Office, 1963), p. 85.
45. Mayer, p. 107.
46. *State Data and State Rankings,* Part 2 of *Health, Education and Welfare Trends,* 1965 Edition (Washington: U. S. Government Printing Office), p. 555.
47. Lawrence, et al., p. 22.
48. *Proposed,* p. 52.
49. *Proposed,* p. 52.
50. Hunt and Huyck, p. 13.
51. Hunt and Huyck, p. 16.
52. Mayer, p. 110.
53. Anselm L. Strauss, "Medical Ghettos," *Trans-action* (May, 1967), p. 8.
54. Mayer, p. 107.
55. Thompson, p. 87.
56. Quoted in Thompson, p. 88.
57. R. C. Scheerenberger, "Mental Retardation: Definition, Classification, and Prevalence," *Mental Retardation Abstracts,* I (Washington: U. S. Government Printing Office, 1964), p. 439.
58. Masland, et al., p. 19.
59. Hardy, p. 44f.
60. See, e.g., Lawrence, et al., *passim.*
61. Thompson, p. 87.
62. Thomas F. Pettigrew, *A Profile of the Negro American* (Princeton, 1964), pp. 88–89.
63. Lawrence, et al., p. 29.
64. *State Data and State Rankings,* p. S55.
65. A. M. Scheib, *Mental Retardation Abstracts,* III (Washington: U. S. Government Printing Office, 1966), No. 1, p.

65. A review of William J. Culley, "Nutrition and Mental Retardation," in *Medical Aspects of Mental Retardation,* ed. Charles H. Carter (Springfield, Ill., 1965).

66. Abramowicz and Kass, p. 9.

67. Quoted in Masland, et al., pp. 62–63.

68. Masland, et al., p. 63.

69. Quoted in Masland, et al., p. 62.

70. R. van Sickle, *Mental Retardation Abstracts,* I (Washington: U. S. Government Printing Office, 1964), p. 506. A review of Stoch and Smythe, "Nutrition of Brain in Infancy," *British Medical Journal,* I (1964), 651f.

71. William J. Culley, quoted in *IARC News* (July, 1967), published by the Indiana Association for the Retarded Children.

72. Harold Jacobziner, "Lead Poisoning in Childhood: Epidemiology, Manifestations, and Prevention," *Clinical Pediatrics,* No. 5 (1966), pp. 277–286.

73. Joseph P. Fried, "Paint-Poison Danger to Children Fought," *The New York Times* (March 2, 1969), Section 8, p. 1.

74. Abramowicz and Kass, pp. 12–16.

75. Kenneth B. Clark, *Dark Ghetto* (New York, 1965), p. 30.

76. Philip R. Dodge, "Application of Knowledge to the Prevention of Mental Retardation," in *Proceedings, The White House Conference on Mental Retardation* (Washington: U. S. Government Printing Office, 1963), p. 110.

77. Claire Hancock, *Children and Neglect* (Washington: U. S. Government Printing Office, 1963), pp. 10–11.

78. Quoted in Oscar Lewis, *La Vida* (New York, 1967), p. 264.

Chapter III: The Effects of Cultural Deprivation on Intellectual Performance

1. Frank Riessman, *The Culturally Deprived Child* (New York, 1962), p. 1.

2. "The Great Cities School Improvement Studies," Ford Foundation Project, mimeographed, 1960, in Riessman, p. 1.

3. *Juvenile Delinquency and Youth Crime,* Task Force on Juvenile Delinquency (Washington: U. S. Government Printing Office, 1967), p. 45.

4. J. McV. Hunt, *Intelligence and Experience* (New York, 1961), pp. 258–259.

5. Irving N. Berlin, "Special Learning Problems of Deprived Children," *NEA Journal,* LV (March, 1966), p. 23.

6. Riessman, p. 37.

7. Berlin, p. 23.

8. Hunt, in Thomas F. Pettigrew, *A Profile of the American Negro* (Princeton, 1964), p. 110.

9. Pettigrew, p. 110.

10. Berlin, p. 23.

11. Martin Deutsch and Bert Brown, "Social Influences in Negro-White Intelligence Differences," *Social Issues* (April, 1964), p. 27, in Moynihan, p. 36.

12. Daniel P. Moynihan, *The Negro Family, The Case for National Action* (Washington: U. S. Government Printing Office, 1965), p. 9.

13. Riessman, p. 36.

14. Kenneth B. Clark, *Dark Ghetto* (New York), pp. 64–65.

15. Oscar Lewis, "The Culture of Poverty," *Scientific American,* CCXV, No. 4 (October, 1966), p. 23.

16. Lee Rainwater, "Crucible of Identity: The Negro Lower-Class Family," *Daedalus* (Winter, 1966), p. 210.

17. Michael Harrington, *The Other America* (Baltimore, 1962), p. 146.

18. Martin Deutsch, "The Disadvantaged Child and the Learning Process," *Education in Depressed Areas,* ed. A. Harry Passow (New York, 1963), p. 171.

19. Charles E. Silberman, *Crisis in Black and White* (New York, 1964), pp. 270–271.

20. L. Aserlind, "Investigation of Maternal Factors Related to the Acquisition of Verbal Skills of Infants in a Culturally Disadvantaged Population," unpublished doctoral dissertation, University of Wisconsin, 1963, in James J. McCarthy, "Research on the Linguistic Problems of the Mentally Retarded," *Mental Retardation Abstracts,* I (1964), p. 17.

21. *Miles to Go* (Connecticut Mental Retardation Planning Project Report, March, 1966), p. 109, footnote 8 (3).

22. Quoted by Imogene D. Cahill, "Child Rearing in the Culture of Poverty," presented at the 1967 Biennial Convention of the National League for Nursing, May 9, 1967, p. 11.

23. *Miles to Go,* p. 109, footnote 8 (4).

24. Robert L. Erdman and James L. Olson, "Relationships Between Educational Programs for the Mentally Retarded and the Culturally Deprived," *Mental Retardation Abstracts,* III, No. 3 (1966), p. 314.

25. Ben H. Bagdikian, *In the Midst of Plenty* (New York, 1964), p. 120.

26. Bagdikian, p. 50.

27. Warren Cutts, "Reading Unreadiness in the Underprivileged," *NEA Journal,* LII (April, 1963), p. 23.

28. Deutsch, "Disadvantaged Child," p. 173.

29. Deutsch, "Disadvantaged Child," p. 171.

30. Deutsch, "Disadvantaged Child," p. 170.

31. Deutsch, "Disadvantaged Child," p. 170.

32. J. McV. Hunt, in Silberman, p. 275.

33. Raintree, p. 203.

34. Miriam Hughes, personal communication with author, May, 1967.

35. R. F. Harrell, E. R. Woodyard, and A. I. Gates, "Influence of Vitamin Supplementation of Diets of Pregnant and Lactating Women on Intelligence of Their Offspring," *Metabolism,* V (1956), pp. 555–562.

36. Mavis B. Stoch, "The Effect of Undernutrition During Infancy on Subsequent Brain Growth and Intellectual Development," mimeographed, Red Cross Hospital, Capetown, South Africa, 1966.

37. Lola M. Irelan, "Health Practices of the Poor," *Low-Income Life Styles,* ed. L. M. Irelan (Washington: U. S. Government Printing Office, 1966), p. 54.

38. Mary Frances Greene and Orletta Ryan, *The Schoolchildren* (New York, 1967), quoted by Peter Schrag, "The Irrelevance of Dick and Jane," *The Nation* (March 21, 1966), p. 336.

39. L. S. Watson [rev. of Delton C. Beier, "Behavior Disturbances in the Mentally Retarded," appearing in *Mental Retardation: A Review of Research,* eds. H. Stevens and R. Heber (Chicago, 1964), pp. 453–487], *Mental Retardation Abstracts,* II (July, September, 1965), p. 387.

40. Harrington, p. 136.

Chapter IV: Public Education and Mental
Retardation: The Self-Fulfilling Prophecy Fulfilled

1. Martin Deutsch, "The Disadvantaged Child and the Learning Process," *Education in Depressed Areas,* ed. A. Harry Passow (New York, 1963), p. 178. This book hereafter referred
to as *Education.*

2. Robert M. MacIver, *Final Report: Juvenile Delinquency
Evaluation Projects* (New York, 1962).

3. Martin Deutsch, *Minority Group and Class Status as Related to Social and Personality Factors in Scholastic Achievement* (Ithaca, N. Y., 1960).

4. Joan I. Roberts, *School Children in the Urban Slum* (New
York, 1967), p. 31.

5. *Equality of Educational Opportunity* (Washington: U. S.
Government Printing Office, 1966), p. 26.

6. Edgar May, *The Wasted Americans* (New York, 1964),
p. 71.

7. May, p. 72.

8. May, p. 75.

9. Russell Kirk, "Poverty of Condition and Poverty of Mind,"
National Review (June, 1965), p. 467.

10. "Editorial: The Subtler Significance of Urban Unrest,"
The American City (October, 1966), p. 8.

11. Kenneth B. Clark, *Dark Ghetto* (New York, 1965), pp.
119–120.

12. Harlem Youth Opportunities Unlimited, Inc., *Youth in
the Ghetto* (New York, 1964), p. 168. Hereafter referred to as
Youth.

13. *Youth,* pp. 169, 170, 179.

14. *Youth,* p. 227.

15. Susan B. Silverman, *Compensatory Education for Cultural Deprivation,* B. S. Bloom, et al. (New York, 1965), p. 74.

16. Gerald Jonas, "Horatio Alger is Dead," *The New York
Times Book Review* (July 16, 1967), p. 6.

17. Patricia Sexton, *Education and Income* (New York,
1961), p. 28.

18. Charles E. Silberman, *Crisis in Black and White* (New
York, 1964), p. 249.

19. Clark, p. 124.

20. Kirk, p. 467.

21. Sexton, p. 101.
22. Silberman, p. 250.
23. Silberman, p. 252.
24. Leonard Buder, "Study Here Finds School Officials Mind in Inertia," *The New York Times* (August 13, 1967), pp. 1, 41.
25. Silberman, p. 257.
26. Personal communication, Governor's Conference on Education, Rutgers University, April 2, 1966.
27. Goodwin Watson, "Foreword," *The Culturally Deprived Child,* Frank Riessman (New York, 1962), p. ix.
28. *A Task Force Study of the Public School System in the District of Columbia As It Relates to the War on Poverty,* conducted by the Committee on Education and Labor of the U. S. House of Representatives (Washington: U. S. Government Printing Office, 1966), p. 39. Hereafter referred to as *A Task Force Study.*
29. Sexton, pp. 85–86.
30. Sexton, p. 235.
31. Sexton, p. 236.
32. Sexton, p. 236.
33. Sexton, p. 228.
34. Nancy L. Arnez, "The Effect of Teacher Attitudes Upon the Culturally Different," *School and Society* (March 19, 1966), p. 149.
35. Sexton, p. 162.
36. Arthur Pearl, "As a Psychologist Sees Pressures on Disadvantaged Teenagers," *NEA Journal* (February, 1965), p. 21. Hereafter referred to as Pearl, "Psychologist Secs Pressures."
37. *Juvenile Delinquency and Youth Crime,* Task Force on Juvenile Delinquency (Washington: U. S. Government Printing Office, 1967), p. 367. Hereafter referred to as *Juvenile Delinquency.*
38. *Juvenile Delinquency,* p. 242.
39. Sexton, p. 83.
40. Brown vs. Board of Education, 347 U. S. 483 (1954).
41. Robert J. Havighurst, "Urban Development and the Educational System," *Education,* ed. A. H. Passow, p. 34.
42. *Juvenile Delinquency,* p. 50.
43. Sexton, p. 31.
44. *The Washington Report,* American Psychological Association, III, No. 4 (June–July, 1967), p. 2.

45. *A Task Force Study,* p. 37.

46. *The Washington Report,* p. 2.

47. Clark, p. 128.

48. A. Harry Passow, "Sociological Aspects of Education in Depressed Areas," *Education,* ed. A. H. Passow, p. 186.

49. Sexton, p. 204.

50. Ben H. Bagdikian, *In the Midst of Plenty* (New York, 1964), p. 11.

51. Sexton, p. 205.

52. Vernon F. Haubrich, "Teachers for Big-City Schools," *Education,* ed. A. H. Passow, p. 245.

53. Mel Ravitz, "The Role of the School in the Urban Setting," *Education,* ed. A. H. Passow, p. 18.

54. Otto Klineberg, "Life is Fun in a Smiling Fair-Skinned World," *The Saturday Review* (February 16, 1963), p. 77.

55. Horace Mann Bond, *Academic Talent Among Underprivileged Populations* (Atlanta, 1967), p. 69.

56. John Niemeyer, "Some Guidelines to Desirable Elementary School Reorganization," *The Disadvantaged Learner: Educating the Disadvantaged Learner,* ed. Staten Webster (San Francisco, 1966), p. 393.

57. Klineberg, p. 77.

58. Klineberg, p. 75.

59. Paul Bullock and Robert Singleton, "The Minority Child and the Schools," *The Progressive,* XXVI (November, 1962), p. 34.

60. *Juvenile Delinquency,* p. 238.

61. Cadwalader Parent-Teacher's Association, *Ethnic Representation in Illustrations and Subject Area Relevance to Environment of Elementary School Texts* (March 15, 1967), p. 6.

62. Plato, *Laches 200.*

63. Ravitz, p. 19.

64. Ronald Sullivan, "Jersey Planning Teachers Corps to Revitalize Schools in Cities," *The New York Times* (August 16, 1967), p. 26.

65. Silberman, p. 263.

66. Haubrich, p. 248.

67. Haubrich, p. 243.

68. Sullivan, p. 26.

69. Sexton, pp. 117, 120.

70. Clark, p. 138.

71. *A Task Force Study,* p. 12.

72. Ravitz, p. 19.

73. Clark, p. 135.

74. Clark, p. 138.

75. Howard Becker, "The Career of the Chicago Public School Teacher," *American Sociological Review* (July, 1952), pp. 470–476.

76. Robert J. Havighurst, *The Public Schools of Chicago* (Chicago, 1963), pp. 341, 346.

77. Sexton, p. 121.

78. Sexton, p. 122.

79. *Equality of Educational Opportunity,* pp. 12, 318.

80. Clark, p. 138.

81. *Juvenile Delinquency,* p. 163.

82. Richard A. Cloward and James A. Jones, "Social Class: Educational Attitudes and Participation," *Education,* ed. A. H. Passow, p. 191.

83. Cloward and Jones, p. 191.

84. Peter Schrag, "The Irrelevance of Dick and Jane," *The Nation* (March 21, 1966), p. 336.

85. Frank Riessman, *The Culturally Deprived Child* (New York, 1962), p. 73.

86. Arthur Pearl, "Youth in Lower-Class Settings," *Problems of Youth,* eds. Muzafer Sherif and Carolyn W. Sherif (Chicago, 1965), p. 96.

87. Haubrich, p. 247.

88. *Juvenile Delinquency,* p. 239.

89. Haubrich, p. 246.

90. "Editorial: Discrimination," *School and Society,* XCIV (November 12, 1966), p. 378.

91. "Editorial: Discrimination," pp. 378–379.

92. Kenneth B. Clark, "Educational Stimulation of Racially Disadvantaged Children," *Education,* ed. A. H. Passow, p. 148.

93. Lawana Trout, "We Ain't Unteachable . . . Just Unteached," *NEA Journal* (April, 1967), pp. 25–26.

94. Pearl, "Psychologist Sees Pressures," p. 21.

95. Clark, *Dark Ghetto,* p. 129.

96. *Juvenile Delinquency,* p. 164.

97. Helen H. Davidson and Gerhard Lang, "Children's Perception of Their Teacher's Feelings Toward Them Related to Self-Perception, School Achievement and Behavior," *Journal of*

Experimental Education (December, 1960), pp. 107–118.
98. George W. Jones, "Compensatory Education for the Disadvantaged," *NEA Journal* (April, 1967), p. 22.
99. Riessman, pp. 22–23.
100. *Juvenile Delinquency,* p. 50.
101. "Editorial: Discrimination," p. 380.
102. Schrag, p. 336.
103. Author's comment, at Camden Special Education School, May, 1967.
104. Schrag, pp. 336–337.
105. Schrag, p. 337.
106. Fred M. Hechinger, "The Teacher Gets What He Expects," *The New York Times* (August 13, 1967), p. E9.
107. Hechinger, p. E9.
108. *Equality of Educational Opportunity,* p. 12.
109. *Equality of Educational Opportunity,* p. 13.
110. *Equality of Educational Opportunity,* p. 14.
111. Sexton, pp. 113–114.
112. *A Task Force Study,* p. 9.
113. *A Task Force Study,* p. 10.
114. Sullivan, p. 26.
115. Marjorie Hunter, "Poor Schools Called a Cause of Riots," *The New York Times* (July 25, 1967), p. 14.

Chapter V: The Health Crisis of the Poor

1. Mrs. Janice Bradshaw, quoted by Theodore M. Berry, "Recent Federal Legislation: Its Meaning for Public Health," *American Journal of Public Health,* LVI, No. 4 (April, 1966), p. 584. *The American Journal of Public Health* will hereafter be cited as *AJPH*.
2. Dr. H. Jack Geiger, "The Poor and the Professional: Who Takes the Handle off the Broad Street Pump?" presented at the 94th Annual Meeting of the American Public Health Association in San Francisco (November 1, 1966), p. 1.
3. Dr. George James, "Poverty as an Obstacle to Health Progress in Our Cities," *AJPH,* LV, No. 11 (November, 1965), p. 1757.
4. Dr. Donald K. Freedman, "Quality of Medical Care and Public Welfare Medical Programs," *AJPH,* LIII, No. 6 (June, 1963), p. 949.
5. Dr. Alonzo S. Yerby, "The Disadvantaged and Health

Care," *AJPH,* LVI, No. 1 (January, 1966), p. 5. Hereafter referred to as Yerby, "Disadvantaged."

6. Geiger, p. 1.

7. Dr. Count D. Gibson, Jr., "The Columbia Point Health Center and Health Association," delivered at the 94th Annual Meeting of the American Public Health Association in San Francisco (November 1, 1966), p. 3.

8. Fred J. Cook, *The Plot Against the Patient* (Englewood Cliffs, N. J., 1967), p. 26.

9. Dr. Alonzo S. Yerby, "Medical Care of the Indigent," *Public Health Reports,* LXXXI, No. 1 (January, 1966), p. 7. Hereafter referred to as Yerby, "Medical."

10. Charlotte Muller, "Income and the Receipt of Medical Care," *AJPH,* LV, No. 4 (April, 1965), p. 512.

11. Dr. Derek Robinson, "Use of Medical Services and Facilities by Welfare-Supported Children," *Public Health Reports,* LXXX, No. 12 (December, 1965), p. 1056.

12. Margaret Olendzki, Dr. Charles H. Goodrich, and Dr. George G. Reader, "The Significance of Welfare Status in the Care of Indigent Patients," *AJPH,* LIII, No. 10 (October, 1963), p. 1678.

13. Dr. Alonzo S. Yerby, "The Problems of Medical Care for Indigent Populations," *AJPH,* LV, No. 8 (August, 1965), p. 1213. Hereafter referred to as Yerby, "Problems."

14. Mitchell I. Ginsberg, quoted in "Ginsberg Says Public Attitudes Run Against Welfare Programs," *The New York Times* (N. D.).

15. Yerby, "Medical," p. 7.

16. Robinson, p. 1057.

17. Thomas A. Johnson, "Life on Welfare: A Daily Struggle for Existence," *The New York Times* (December 19, 1966), p. 54.

18. Lola M. Irelan, "Health Practices of the Poor." *Low-Income Life Styles,* ed. L. M. Irelan (Washington: U. S. Government Printing Office, 1966), p. 54.

19. Yerby, "Disadvantaged," p. 5.

20. James, p. 1758.

21. James, p. 1763.

22. James, p. 1763.

23. James, p. 1764.

24. James, p. 1764.

25. Bayard Rustin, "A Way Out of the Exploding Ghetto," *The New York Times Magazine* (August 13, 1967), p. 59.

26. Jack T. Conway, "The Beneficiary, the Consumer— What He Needs and Wants," *AJPH*, LV, No. 11.

27. James, p. 1762.

28. James, p. 1762.

29. Conway, p. 1783.

30. Institute of Industrial Relations, University of California at Los Angeles, findings cited by Cook, p. 72.

31. Cook, p. 69.

32. Robinson, p. 1059.

33. Yerby, "Disadvantaged," p. 5.

34. Geraldine A. Gleeson and Elijah L. White, "Disability and Medical Care Among Whites and Nonwhites in the United States," *Health, Education and Welfare Indicators* (Washington: U. S. Government Printing Office, October, 1965), pp. 1–10, reviewed in *Medical Care Review* (January, 1967). Dr. Kenneth W. Clement, "The Health Concerns of the Negro— Today and for the Future," Centennial Conference on the Health Status of the Negro Today and in the Future, Howard University, Washington, D. C. (March 13–14, 1967), p. 11. Conference will hereafter be referred to as Centennial Conference.

35. Dr. Helen M. Wallace, Dr. Victor Eisner, and Dr. Samuel Dooley, "Availability and Usefulness of Selected Health and Socioeconomic Data for Community Planning," *AJPH*, LVII, No. 5 (May, 1967), p. 770.

36. Edward G. Stockwell, "Use of Socioeconomic Status as a Demographic Variable," *Public Health Reports*, LXXXI, No. 11 (November, 1966), p. 965.

37. A. Donabedian and L. S. Rosenfeld, "Prenatal Care in Metropolitan Boston," *AJPH*, XLVIII, No. 9 (September, 1958), pp. 1115–1124, findings summarized by Muller, p. 517.

38. G. H. T. Kimble, quoted by Berry, p. 583.

39. Earl Lomon Koos, *The Health of Regionville* (New York, 1954), pp. 112–116.

40. "Medical Care, Health Status and Family Income" (Washington: U. S. Government Printing Office, 1964), p. 6. Hereafter referred to as "Medical Care."

41. "Medical Care," p. 9.

42. "Medical Care," p. 12.

43. "Medical Care," p. 13.
44. "Medical Care," p. 20.
45. Anselm L. Strauss, "Medical Ghettos," *Trans-action* (May, 1967), p. 10.
46. "Medical Care," p. 45.
47. Cited in Muller, p. 511.
48. "Medical Care," p. 51.
49. "Medical Care," p. 24.
50. "Medical Care," p. 24.
51. "Medical Care," p. 51.
52. "Medical Care," p. 29.
53. "Medical Care," p. 30.
54. Sam Shapiro, et al., "Further Observations on Prematurity and Perinatal Mortality in a General Population and in the Population of a Prepaid Group Practice Medical Care Plan," *AJPH*, L, No. 9 (September, 1960), pp. 1305–1306. Findings summarized by Muller, p. 516.
55. Breslow, Lester, and Hochstim, "Socio-cultural Aspects of Cervical Cytology in Alameda County, California," *Public Health Reports,* LXXIX, No. 2 (February, 1964), p. 110.
56. "Medical Care," p. 38.
57. "Medical Care," p. 35.
58. Patricia Sexton, *Education and Income* (New York, 1961), p. 101.
59. Sexton, p. 101.
60. Sexton, p. 103.
61. Sexton, p. 103.
62. Sexton, p. 104.
63. Sexton, p. 100.
64. Sexton, p. 99.
65. Sexton, p. 99.
66. Dr. Charles Mayo, quoted by Dr. Howard A. Rusk, "Poverty and Health," *The New York Times* (August 13, 1967), p. 69.
67. Bureau of Labor Statistics, findings cited by Rusk.
68. James, p. 1764.
69. Muller, p. 510.
70. G. H. Bigelow and H. F. Lombard, *Cancer and Other Chronic Diseases in Massachusetts* (Boston, 1933).
71. R. H. Britten and I. Altman, "Illness and Accident

Among Persons Living Under Different Housing Conditions," data based on the National Health Survey, *Public Health Reports,* LVI (1941), pp. 609–640.

72. "Medical Care," p. 53.

73. "Medical Care," p. 55.

74. "Medical Care," p. 60.

75. "Medical Care," p. 57.

76. "Medical Care," p. 71.

77. Lilian Guralnick, "Selected Family Characteristics and Health Measures Reported in the Health Interview Survey," in *Family Characteristics and Health Measures* (Washington: U. S. Government Printing Office, 1967), p. 6.

78. P. S. Lawrence, "Chronic Illness and Socio-Economic Status," *Public Health Reports,* LXIII, No. 47 (November 19, 1948), p. 1514.

79. Lawrence, p. 1521.

80. Lawrence, p. 1518.

81. Robert Straus, "Poverty as an Obstacle to Health Progress in Our Rural Areas," *AJPH,* LV, No. 11 (November, 1965), p. 1776.

82. Dr. Charles H. Goodrich, Margaret Olendzki, and Dr. George G. Reader, "The New York Hospital-Cornell Medical Center: A Progress Report on an Experiment in Welfare Medical Care," *AJPH,* LV, No. 1 (January, 1965), p. 93.

83. Dr. Shirley A. Mayer, "Maternal and Infant Care Project in Newark, N. J.: A Progress Report," *Public Health News,* XLVIII, No. 5 (May, 1967), p. 109.

84. Robinson, p. 1059.

85. Yerby, "Problems," p. 1214.

86. James, p. 1759.

87. Lisle C. Cartér, "Possible Solutions and Recommendations," Centennial Conference, p. 48.

88. Muller, p. 519.

89. Judith Krugman, "Cultural Deprivation and Child Development," *High Points,* XXXVIII (November, 1956).

90. August B. Hollingshead and F. C. Redlich, *Social Class and Mental Illness* (New York, 1958).

91. L. Strole, T. S. Langer, S. T. Michael, M. K. Opler, and T. A. C. Rennie, *Mental Health in the Metropolis: The Midtown Manhattan Study* (New York, 1962).

92. Michael Harrington, *The Other America* (Baltimore, 1962), p. 136.

93. Harrington, p. 132.

94. Koos, p. 25.

95. Koos, p. 37.

96. Koos, pp. 139, 142.

97. Housewife, quoted by Koos, p. 36.

98. Irelan, p. 59.

99. Irelan, p. 55.

100. Housewife, quoted by Koos, p. 35, and by Irelan, p. 57.

101. Goodrich, et al., p. 91, and James, p. 1765.

102. Jerry A. Solon, "Patterns of Medical Care: Sociocultural Variations Among a Hospital's Outpatients," *AJPH,* LVI, No. 6 (June, 1966), p. 865.

103. Muller, p. 517.

104. A. Strauss, p. 12.

105. A. Strauss, p. 8.

106. Dr. Wilbur Hoff, "Why Health Programs are not Reaching the Unresponsive in Our Communities," *Public Health News,* XLVII, No. 11 (November, 1966), p. 260.

107. "Welfare and Health Practices—Handout or Outreach," in Economic Opportunity in Cities, U. S. Conference of Mayors (January, 1966), p. 70.

108. Koos, p. 35.

109. Dr. James G. Haughton, "Major Health Problems of the Negro," Centennial Conference, p. 32.

110. "Welfare and Health Practices—Handout or Outreach," p. 70.

111. Dr. Lewis D. Polk, cited in "Cost Is Chief Obstacle to Prenatal Care," *Public Health Reports,* LXXX, No. 2 (February, 1965), p. 103.

112. Gibson, p. 2.

113. "Medical Program Goes Into Homes," *The New York Times* (March 5, 1967).

114. *Northeast Neighborhood Association Report* (N. D.), p. 7.

115. Dorothy D. Harrison, "Summary and Recommendations," Centennial Conference, p. 76.

116. "Reaching 'Hard-to-Reach' Families," *Currents in Public Health,* V (July–August, 1965), p. 1.

117. A. L. Sandusky, *Children,* VIII (1961), p. 93, quoted in above source, p. 1.

118. Polk, p. 102.

119. Conway, p. 1784.

120. "Disadvantaged," p. 8.

121. Dr. Alfred Haynes and Dr. Paul M. Densen, "Implications for Research about the Health of the Negro," Centennial Conference, p. 40.

122. Rene Dubos, quoted by R. Straus, p. 1775.

123. Carter, p. 49.

124. R. Straus, p. 1775.

125. R. Straus, p. 1775.

126. "The Living is 'Inhuman,'" *The New York Times* (August 27, 1967), p. 2E.

127. *State Data and State Ranking,* p. S1.

128. John W. Gardner, quoted in *Cities in Crisis, The Challenge of Change* (Washington: U. S. Government Printing Office, 1967).

129. Rusk, p. 69.

130. Lewis Heber, *Crisis in Our Cities* (Englewood Cliffs, N. J., 1965), p. 2.

131. Dr. John B. Calhoun, National Institute of Mental Health, findings cited by Herber, p. 7.

132. Dr. Ellis D. Sox, cited in "Unenforced Codes Create Slums," *Public Health Reports,* LXXX, No. 2 (February, 1965), pp. 100–101.

133. Sox, p. 100.

134. James Henderson, "Summary and Recommendations," Centennial Conference, pp. 84–85.

135. Cook, p. 33.

136. Muller, p. 518.

137. Clement, p. 15.

138. A. J. Harmon, cited in "Would Blend Health Plan With Urban Renewal," *Public Health Reports,* LXXIX, No. 3 (March, 1964), p. 211.

139. Gibson, p. 1.

140. Freedman, p. 945.

141. Dr. Leonard J. Duhl, "Urbanization and Human Needs," *AJPH,* LIU, No. 5 (May, 1964), pp. 724, 726.

142. Duhl, "Urbanization, Poverty, and Health," *Bulletin*

of the New York Academy of Science, Second Series, XLII, No. 5 (May, 1966), p. 370.

143. James A. Kent and C. Harvey Smith, "Involving the Urban Poor in Health Services Through Accommodation—The Employment of Neighborhood Representatives," *AJPH,* LVII, No. 6 (June, 1967), p. 1002.

144. M. I. Roemer, "Medical Care Administration in the United States," *AJPH,* LII (January, 1962), p. 8.

145. Dr. Conrad Siepp, cited in "Only One Hospital in Seven Offers Social Services," *Public Health Reports,* LXXIX, No. 3 (March, 1964), p. 226.

146. Berry, p. 584.

147. Yerby, "Problems," p. 1212.

148. James, p. 1760.

149. Yerby, "Problems," p. 1213.

150. Clement, p. 14.

151. Dr. Lorin E. Kerr, "Summary and Recommendations," Centennial Conference, p. 89.

152. "Special Health Problems in Preschoolers," *Currents in Public Health,* V (April, 1965), p. 3.

153. Dr. Milton Terris, cited in "Medical Schools Balk Preventive Care," *Public Health Reports,* LXXIX, No. 3 (March, 1964), p. 227.

154. Clement, p. 13.

155. "New or Expanded Health Services; Reorganization of Ambulatory Medical Care," N. J. Department of Health Memorandum (February 8, 1967), p. 1.

156. "Commissioner's Study Committee on Delivery of Ambulatory and Related Health Services and Medical Care to the Disadvantaged," N. J. Department of Health Memorandum (December 9, 1966), p. 1.

157. *State Data and State Ranking,* p. S-73.

158. I. S. Falk, "Medical Care and Social Policy," *AJPH,* LV, No. 4 (April, 1965), p. 525.

159. Martin Tolchin, "Copter's Mercy Mission: Craft Lands in Central Park with Critically Ill Boy," *The New York Times* (July 28, 1967), p. 27.

160. Yerby, "Disadvantaged," p. 8.

161. "Child Health Services and the Underprivileged," *Currents in Public Health,* VI (October, 1966), p. 1.

162. "Child Health Services," p. 3.

163. Dr. E. Richard Weincrman, Robert S. Ratner, Dr. Anthony Robbins, and Marvin A. Lavenhar, "Yale Studies in Ambulatory Medical Care v. Determinants of Use of Hospital Emergency Services," *AJPH*, LVI, No. 7 (July, 1966), p. 1054.

164. Solon, p. 887.

165. Clement, p. 13.

166. Irelan, p. 56.

167. Geiger, pp. 1–2.

168. L. Corsa and J. Jessup, "Tax-Supported Medical Care for California's Children," *California Medicine*, XCVI (February, 1962), p. 2.

169. Polk, p. 102.

170. Mayer, p. 107.

171. A. Strauss, *Medical Organization, Medical Care, and Lower Income Groups*, paper prepared for the Institute for Policy Studies, 1967, p. 52.

172. Cook, pp. 69–70.

173. Duhl, "Urbanization and Human Needs," p. 722.

174. Yerby, "Disadvantaged," p. 6.

175. Yerby, "Problems," p. 1213.

176. Duhl, "Urbanization and Human Needs," p. 721.

177. James, p. 1770.

178. Duhl, "Urbanization and Human Needs," p. 721.

179. Mother, quoted by A. Strauss, "Medical Ghettos," p. 10.

180. Lower-class respondent, quoted by Koos, p. 78.

181. *Northeast Neighborhood Association Report*, p. 5.

182. Cook, pp. 31–32.

183. A. Strauss, *Medical Organization, Medical Care, and Lower Income Groups*, p. 63.

184. Dr. Joel J. Alpert, Dr. John Kosa, and Dr. Robert J. Haggerty, "Medical Help and Maternal Nursing Care in the Life of Low-Income Families," *Pediatrics*, XXXIX, No. 5 (May, 1967), p. 749.

185. Solon, p. 893.

186. Conway, p. 1784.

187. Harrison, p. 76.

188. Dr. M. Y. Heshmat, "Summary and Recommendations," Centennial Conference, p. 66.

189. "Welfare and Health Practices—Handout or Outreach," p. 77.

190. Dorothy D. Watts, "Factors Related to the Acceptance of Modern Medicine," *AJPH,* LVI, No. 8 (August, 1966), p. 1207.

191. A. Strauss, "Medical Ghettos," p. 10.

192. A. Strauss, "Medical Ghettos," p. 11.

193. Columbia Point resident, quoted by Geiger, p. 4.

194. Lower-class respondent, quoted by Koos, p. 93.

195. Social worker, quoted by A. Strauss, "Medical Ghettos," p. 11.

196. Yerby, "Disadvantaged," p. 6.

197. Freedman, p. 946.

198. Freedman, p. 946.

199. Doctor, quoted by Cook, p. 269.

200. Martin Tolchin, "Medical Abuses Laid to Doctors," *The New York Times* (August 16, 1967), p. 1.

201. Haughton, cited by Tolchin, "Medical Abuses Laid to Doctors," p. 1.

202. Dr. Michael J. Halberstam, "A Doctor's Diagnosis of Medicare," *The New York Times Magazine* (August 13, 1967), p. 19.

203. Louis Cassels, "A Year After Its Birth, Medicare Works So Well Doctors Like It," *Trenton Evening Times* (June 22, 1967), p. 42.

204. Dr. Milton Cherkasky, quoted by Halberstam, p. 15.

205. Value Line Investment Survey and Clifford D. McGinn, respectively, quoted by Douglas W. Cray, "Health Industry Weighs Medicare," *The New York Times* (July 2, 1967), p. F11.

206. H. J. Maidenberg, "Health Insurers Discover a New Friend—Medicare," *The New York Times* (July 2, 1967), p. F1.

207. "Blue Cross Finances Improve," *Trenton Evening Times* (March 2, 1967).

208. "Blue Cross Outpatient Plan Rapped," *Trenton Evening Times* (January 3, 1967).

209. John Kolesar, "Blue Shield Rates Up, Up, Up," *Trenton Evening Times* (March 23, 1967), p. 17.

210. Bureau of Labor Statistics, Consumer Price Index, cited by Maidenberg, p. F11.

211. "Grant Explains Rising Costs As Hospital Week is Marked," *Hunterdon County Democrat* (May 4, 1967).

212. Martin Tolchin, "It's Still Doctors vs. Medicaid," *The New York Times* (April 6, 1967).

213. Seymour R. Thaler, quoted by Tolchin, "Hospitals Scored for Rising Fees," *The New York Times* (August 28, 1967), p. 33.

214. "State Sees a Cut in Medicaid Rolls Under U. S. Action," *The New York Times* (August 21, 1967), p. 24.

215. Richard Harris, *A Sacred Trust* (New York, 1966).

216. Official in the Department of Health, Education and Welfare, quoted by Cook, p. 265.

217. United Nations World Health Organization, findings cited by Cook, p. 27.

218. Falk, p. 524.

219. "California Cuts Health Programs," *The New York Times* (August 17, 1967), p. 41.

220. Yerby, "Problems," p. 1212.

221. Yerby, "Disadvantaged," pp. 6–7.

222. George F. Gilder and Bruce K. Chapman, *The Party That Lost Its Head* (New York, 1966), p. 294.

223. J. William Fulbright, "The Great Society is a Sick Society," *The New York Times Magazine* (August 20, 1967), p. 95.

224. Fulbright, p. 30.

Chapter VI: Welfare: The Cycle of Dependency

1. Senator Robert F. Kennedy, address to the Day Care Council of New York (May 8, 1967), p. 3.

2. Charles E. Silberman, *The Myths of Automation* (New York, 1966), pp. 83–84.

3. *Statement of Objectives* (New Jersey Division of Public Welfare, 1966), p. 1.

4. *Summary of Recommendations to the Secretary of Health, Education and Welfare,* The Advisory Council on Public Welfare (June 29, 1966), pp. 6–7. Hereafter referred to as *Summary of Recommendations*.

5. Richard A. Cloward and Frances Fox Piven, "Starving by the Rule Book," *The Nation,* CCIV (April 3, 1967), pp. 429–431.

6. Isadore Silver, "Poverty As a Crime," *Commonwealth,* LXXXV (October 21, 1966), p. 74.

7. Martin Rein, "Social Science and the Elimination of Poverty," *Journal of the American Institute of Planners,* XXXIII (May, 1967), p. 160.

8. *Summary of Recommendations,* p. 6.

9. Georgina M. Smith, *On the Welfare* (New Brunswick, N. J., 1967), p. 3.

10. *Report of the Senate Fact Finding Committee on Labor and Welfare: Aid to Needy Children Program,* 1961, p. 48.

11. *Report of the Findings and Recommendations Related to the Public Assistance Program of the Monmouth County Welfare Board,* conducted by Greenleigh Associates, Inc. (New York, 1963), p. 18. Hereafter referred to as *Report of the Findings.*

12. Personal communication, Mr. Gerald Malanga, public welfare consultant, New Jersey Division of Public Welfare, July 11, 1967.

13. *Public Assistance; Rights and Responsibilities,* prepared by the New Jersey Community Action Training Institute (February, 1967), p. 12.

14. James N. Morgan, Martin H. David, Wilbur J. Cohen, and Harry E. Brazer, *Income and Welfare in the United States* (New York, 1962), pp. 3–4.

15. Joseph A. Califano, address to the Washington Chapter of Sigma Delta Chi, April 19, 1967.

16. "The Relation of New Jersey's War on Poverty to Rising Costs and Caseloads," New Jersey Office of Economic Opportunity Background Memorandum (February 24, 1967), pp. 1, 2, 5.

17. 1965 Annual Report, New Jersey Department of Institutions and Agencies, in *The Welfare Reporter,* XVII, No. 3 (July, 1966), p. 30.

18. Bernard P. Indik, *The Motivation to Work* (New Brunswick, N. J., N. D.), p. 4.

19. Smith, p. 5.

20. Martin, p. 5.

21. Smith, p. 39.

22. Martin, p. 9.

23. *Statement of Objectives,* pp. 2–4.

24. Bert Hunter, "The Case for the Aid to Dependent Children Program," *New Jersey Welfare Council Bulletin,* XXXVI (December, 1966), p. 2.

25. *Report of the Findings,* p. 31.

26. *Report of the Findings,* p. 27.

27. *Report of the Findings,* p. 4.

28. *Summary of Recommendations,* p. 5.

29. *Report of the Findings,* pp. 46–48.

30. Annette O'Flaherty, in Smith, p. 65.

31. Kathleen Teltsch, "Welfare Services for Problem Children Under Study," *The New York Times* (June 29, 1967), pp. 45, 48.

32. Personal visit by author.

33. Vaughn Davis Bornet, *Welfare in America* (Norman, Oklahoma, 1960), p. 30.

Chapter VII: Food Assistance Programs

1. *Malnutrition and Federal Food Service Programs,* Hearings Before the Committee on Education and Labor, U. S. House of Representatives, Part 1, U. S. Government Printing Office, Washington, D. C., 1968.

2. *Hunger and Malnutrition in America,* Hearings Before the Subcommittee on Employment, Manpower and Poverty of the Committee on Labor and Public Welfare, U. S. Senate, U. S. Government Printing Office, Washington, D. C., July 11 and 12, 1967.

3. *Nutrition and Human Needs,* Hearings Before the Select Committee on Nutrition and Human Needs of the United States Senate, Part 1, U. S. Government Printing Office, Washington, D. C., 1968.

4. Dr. Thomas E. Bryant, M.D., Testimony Before the Senate Select Committee on Nutrition and Human Needs, Prepared Statement. (Publication of hearings unavailable at this date.) January 9, 1969.

5. *Nutrition and Human Needs,* Hearings, Part 1, 1968.

6. *Hungry Children,* Special Report Southern Regional Council, Atlanta, Georgia, 1967, pp. 4–6.

7. *Hunger, U.S.A.,* A Report by the Citizen's Board of Inquiry into Hunger and Malnutrition in the United States, New Community Press, Washington, D. C., 1968.

8. Arnold E. Schaefer, M.D., Testimony Before the Senate

Committee on Nutrition and Human Needs of the United States Senate, Prepared Statement. (Publication of hearings unavailable at this date.) January 22, 1969.

9. Homer Bigart, "Senate Unit Told of Hunger in U. S.," *The New York Times,* January 23, 1969, p. 1.

10. *Hunger, U.S.A.,* p. 17.

11. John A. Churchill, M.D., *Hunger and Malnutrition in the United States,* Hearings Before the Subcommittee on Employment, Manpower and Poverty of the Committee on Labor and Public Welfare, U. S. Senate, U. S. Government Printing Office, Washington, D. C., May, June, 1968, p. 175.

12. Charles U. Lowe, M.D., *Nutrition, Child Care and Public Policy,* Food Industries Advisory Committee, The Nutrition Foundation, Inc., Naples, Florida, February 2, 1968, p. 10.

13. John A. Churchill, M.D., *Hunger and Malnutrition in the United States,* p. 175.

14. Ben H. Bagdikian, *In the Midst of Plenty,* New York, 1964, p. 47.

15. Robert Coles, M.D., *Hunger and Malnutrition in America,* p. 25.

16. Rene Dubos, *So Human an Animal,* Charles Scribner's, New York, 1968, p. 86.

17. Editorial, "The Hungry Are Heard," *The New York Times,* February 24, 1969, p. 36.

18. Robert B. Choate, "Hunger and Malnutrition Among the American Poor—Background Data for Constructive Action in 1969," National Institute of Public Affairs, Washington, D. C., February 1, 1969, p. 13.

19. Elizabeth B. Drew, "Going Hungry in America," *Atlantic Monthly,* December, 1968, p. 54.

20. *Hunger and Malnutrition in the United States,* p. 205.

21. Howard A. Rusk, "Poverty and Health," *The New York Times,* August 13, 1967.

22. *Hunger, U.S.A.,* p. 62.

23. Homer Bigart, "Hunger in America: Mississippi Delta," *The New York Times,* February 18, 1969, p. 18.

24. Homer Bigart, "Hunger in America: Mexicans and Indians Its Stoical Victims," *The New York Times,* February 19, 1969, p. 29.

25. Drew, p. 54.

26. Drew, p. 55.

27. *Hunger, U.S.A.,* p. 50.

28. United States Department of Agriculture, personal communication.

29. "The Hunger Problem and How One Town Is Beating It," *U. S. News and World Report,* February 10, 1969, p. 54.

30. Florence Robin, "Their Daily Bread," in *Hunger in America* (Chronology and Selected Background Materials), Subcommittee on Employment, Manpower and Poverty of the Committee on Labor and Public Welfare, U. S. Senate, U. S. Government Printing Office, Washington, D. C., 1968, p. 102.

31. *Establishment of the Select Committee on Nutrition and Human Needs,* Subcommittee on Employment, Manpower and Poverty of the Committee on Labor and Public Welfare, U. S. Senate, U. S. Government Printing Office, Washington, D. C., September, 1968, p. 9.

32. Robin, p. 102.

33. Choate, p. 15.

34. *Establishment of the Select Committee on Nutrition and Human Needs,* p. 9.

35. John C. Bullitt, "Status of Food Assistance Programs in New Jersey" (unpublished report, May 19, 1966), p. 41.

36. Personal communication with Mrs. Miriam Hughes, director, New Jersey School Lunch Programs, Trenton, N. J., March 19, 1969.

37. *Hunger, U.S.A.,* p. 68.

38. Robert B. Semple, Jr., "$1—Billion Sought to Attack Hunger," *The New York Times,* March 18, 1969, p. 20.

Chapter VIII: Newark: A Case Study of Urban Poverty

1. *New Jersey: Garden State or Urban State,* Conference of New Jersey Association of Architects, Professor Tempko, panelist, Princeton University, Princeton, N. J., p. 81.

2. Russell Sackett, "In a Grim City," *Life Magazine,* LXIII, No. 4 (July 28, 1967), p. 27.

3. Senator Edward Brooke, "What Next?" *Time Magazine,* XC, No. 6 (August 11, 1967), p. 11.

4. *New Jersey: Garden State or Urban State,* Professor Tempko, p. 82.

5. *New Jersey: Garden State or Urban State,* George Rockrise, pp. 92–93.

6. Sackett, p. 27.

7. *Newark, New Jersey, Model Cities Application,* "Part 2— Problem Definition and Analysis, A Community Description," p. 3. Hereafter referred to as *Model.*

8. "Sparks of Tinder," *Time Magazine,* XC, No. 3 (July 21, 1967), p. 21.

9. Mayor John Lindsay, *The New York Times* (August 13, 1967), p. 1.

10. Lindsay, p. 40.

11. *The New York Times* (July 23, 1967), p. E1.

12. Oscar Lewis, *La Vida* (New York, 1967), p. xiv.

13. Raymond Moley, "Newark—Subsidies for Slums," *Bethlehem Globe-Times* (August 5, 1967), p. 27.

14. Jay Rumney and Sara Shuman, *The Cost of Slums in Newark,* pamphlet prepared for the Housing Authority of the City of Newark, 1946, pp. 6–9.

15. Rumney and Shuman, pp. 7, 16.

16. *Model,* p. 3.

17. *Model,* p. 5.

18. *Model,* p. 6.

19. Rumney and Shuman, p. 4.

20. *Model,* p. 64.

21. *Model,* p. 2.

22. *Model,* p. 61.

23. Dr. Aaron A. Haskin, *Sunday Star Ledger* (August 6, 1967), Section 1, p. 12.

24. Haskin.

25. *Rebuilding Newark* (Housing Authority of the City of Newark, October, 1952), pp. 18–20.

26. *The New York Times* (July 16, 1967), p. E1.

27. "Sparks of Tinder," *Time Magazine,* XC, No. 3 (July 21, 1967), p. 21.

28. *Model,* p. 48.

29. *Model,* p. 47.

30. Moley, p. 27.

31. Daniel P. Moynihan, "The Urban Crisis: The Causes and a Plan of Action," *Newark Sunday News* (August 6, 1967), p. 7.

32. *Model,* p. 36.

33. *The New York Times* (August 17, 1967), p. 27.

34. *The New York Times* (August 17, 1967), p. 27.

35. *Model,* p. 36.
36. *Model,* p. 32.
37. *Model,* p. 32.
38. John C. Bullitt, "Status of Food Assistance in New Jersey" (May 19, 1966), p. 40. (Unpublished report.)
39. Bullitt, p. 3.
40. *Model,* pp. 22–23.
41. *Model,* p. 24.
42. *Model,* p. 25.
43. *Rebuilding Newark,* p. 2.
44. *Model,* p. 26.
45. *Model,* p. 27.
46. *Model,* p. 27.
47. *Model,* p. 26.
48. *Model,* p. 30.
49. *Model,* p. 31.
50. *Model,* p. 32.
51. *Model,* p. 33.
52. Georgina M. Smith, *On the Welfare* (New Brunswick, N. J., 1967), p. 7.
53. Smith, p. 7.
54. Smith, p. 51.
55. Smith, p. 51.
56. Smith, p. 17.
57. Smith, p. 65.
58. *Model,* p. 60.
59. *Model,* p. 60.
60. *Newark Star-Ledger* (August 8, 1967), p. 5.
61. *Newark Star-Ledger* (August 8, 1967), p. 5.
62. *Newark Star-Ledger* (August 8, 1967), p. 5.
63. *Newark Star-Ledger* (August 8, 1967), p. 5.
64. *Model,* pp. 8–9.
65. The material in the paragraph preceding this footnote is taken from *Report of City-Wide Testing Program* (Newark Board of Education, October, 1964), p. 3.

Chapter IX: The Migrants: A Case Study of Rural Poverty

1. "Migratory Labor in American Agriculture," President's Committee on Migratory Labor, 1951, in *Children in Migrant*

Families (United States Children's Bureau, December, 1960), p. 2.

2. *New Jersey Farm Labor Report* (Bureau of Farm Placement, Division of Employment Security, 1966), Chart 1.

3. Richard A. Hogarty, *New Jersey Farmers and Migrant Housing Rules* (New York, 1965), p. 8.

4. Robert Coles, *The Migrant Farmer* (Atlanta, 1965), pp. 21, 23.

5. Migrant worker, quoted by Dale Wright, *They Harvest Despair* (Boston, 1965), p. 22.

6. "The Migratory Farm Labor Problem in the United States" (Senate Committee on Labor and Public Welfare, Subcommittee on Migratory Labor, 1965), p. 1.

7. Editorial, "Inching Toward Adequacy," *The New York Times* (September 25, 1966).

8. "Who is the Migrant Child?" (National Committee on the Education of Migrant Children, New York, N. D.), p. 2.

9. "Report of the New Jersey Governor's Task Force on Migrant Farm Labor" (June, 1967), p. 8. Hereafter referred to as "Governor's Task Force."

10. Craciela Delgado, C. L. Brumback, and Mary Brice Deaver, "Eating Patterns Among Migrant Families," *Public Health Reports,* LXXVI, No. 4 (April, 1961), p. 353.

11. *Children in Migrant Families,* p. 36.

12. "1966 Annual Report" (New Jersey Migrant Health Program, New Jersey State Department of Health), p. 8.

13. "Governor's Task Force," p. 2.

14. Migrant ministry worker, quoted in "The Migratory Farm Labor Problem," p. 5.

15. Truman Moore, "Slaves for Rent," *Atlantic Monthly,* CCXV, No. 5 (May, 1965), p. 114.

16. Moore, p. 120.

17. Ben H. Bagdikian, *In the Midst of Plenty* (New York, 1964), pp. 96–97.

18. Ronald Sullivan, "Unions and Vista Drop Aid to Jersey Migrants," *The New York Times* (June 11, 1967), p. 36.

19. "Migrant Workers' Lot Better," *Newark News* (September 22, 1966).

20. Michael Harrington, *The Other America* (Baltimore, 1962), p. 60.

21. Bagdikian, p. 90.
22. Wright, Preface.
23. Wright, p. 9.
24. Coles, p. 4.
25. John Steinbeck, *The Grapes of Wrath* (New York, 1939), p. 477.
26. Bagdikian, p. 90.
27. "The Migratory Farm Labor Problem," p. 40
28. "The Migratory Farm Labor Problem," p. 3.
29. Harrington, p. 48.
30. Harrington, p. 62.
31. Otis Dudley Duncan and James D. Cowhib, "Social Backgrounds and Occupational Commitment of Male Wage-workers in Agriculture," *Agricultural Economics Report,* XVIII, No. 4 (October, 1966), p. 131.
32. Coles, p. 28.
33. Moore, p. 112.
34. Harrington, pp. 47, 65.
35. *New Jersey Farm Labor Report,* p. 4.
36. "Who is the Migrant Child?" p. 3.
37. Moore, p. 119.
38. Richard J. Hughes, Governor, Message to the Staff of New Jersey Migrant Opportunity Program, 1965, p. 1.
39. Hogarty, p. 4.
40. Philip Alampi, quoted in Hogarty, p. 14.
41. John T. McGowan, "Bullitt Denies Poverty Agency Recruiting Blueberry Pickers," *Newark News* (July 21, 1966), p. 13.
42. "1966 Annual Report," p. 8.
43. Israel Tumin, *The Summer School Program for Migrant Children: An Evaluation* (New Jersey Office of Economic Opportunity, 1966), p. 29.
44. Eugene R. Eisman, "Farm Labor Board Raked, Migrant Plight Described," *Camden Courier-Post* (September 9, 1966).
45. Thomas F. Lynch, quoted by Eisman.
46. Mrs. Irene H. Smith, quoted in " 'Tobacco' Conditions Exist at Wenonah Migrant Farm, Seek State Probe of Labor Units," *Paterson News* (August 4, 1966).
47. Personal communication to author by migrant summer schoolteacher, July, 1966.

48. "Governor's Task Force," p. 1.

49. "Governor's Task Force," p. 3.

50. "Governor's Task Force," p. 5.

51. "Governor's Task Force," p. 8.

52. Sullivan, p. 36.

53. Louisa Rossiter Shotwell, *This is the Migrant* (Friendship Press, 1958), p. 3.

54. *Report and Recommendations of the Consultation on Services to Children in the East Coast* (Avon Park, Florida, February 1–3, 1965), p. 10.

55. Shirley E. Greene, *The Education of Migrant Children* (Washington, Department of Rural Education, 1954), p. 29.

56. Tumin, p. 22.

57. Coles, p. 6.

58. Shotwell, p. 2.

59. Mrs. Bernice Shepard, quoted by David C. Schreiber, "Added Burden of Migrants," *Newark News* (April 3, 1966).

60. "1966 Annual Report," pp. 9–10.

61. Kurt W. Back and David J. Pittman, "Dimensions of Mobility," *Mobility and Mental Health,* ed. Mildred B. Kantor (Springfield, Ill., 1965), p. 205.

62. H. B. M. Murphy, "Migration and the Major Mental Disorders: A Reappraisal," *Mobility and Mental Health,* ed. Mildred B. Kantor, p. 5.

63. Coles, p. 27.

64. Coles, p. 26.

65. Charles A. Gilmore, "An Experiment in Migrant Worker Development" (United States Department of Labor, Manpower Administration, December, 1965), p. 4.

66. Coles, p. 11.

67. Coles, p. 26.

68. R. H. Browning and T. J. Northcutt, Jr., "On the Season" (Florida State Board of Health, Monograph Number 2, 1961), p. 46.

69. Browning and Northcutt, p. 51.

70. Browning and Northcutt, p. 27.

71. Browning and Northcutt, p. 49.

72. Browning and Northcutt, p. 50.

73. "1966 Annual Report," p. 40.

74. James K. Shafer, Donald Harting, and Helen L. John-

ston, "Health Needs of Seasonal Farm Workers and Their Families," *Public Health Reports,* LXXVI, No. 6 (June, 1961), p. 469.

75. American Public Health Association, in "The Migratory Farm Labor Problem," p. 10.

76. Moore, p. 112.

77. Wright, p. 94.

78. Moore, p. 113.

79. "The Migratory Farm Labor Problem," p. viii.

80. "The Migratory Farm Labor Problem," p. 38.

81. Wright, p. 81.

82. Harrison Williams, quoted by Moore, p. 114.

83. Migrant worker, quoted in Shafer, et al., p. 410.

84. Moore, p. 114.

85. E. Quimby and A. B. Lemmon, "Parathion Residues as a Cause of Poisoning in Crop Workers," *Journal of the American Medical Association,* CLXVI (February 15, 1958), pp. 741–746, in Shafer, et al., p. 470.

86. "Meeting the Housing Needs of the Poor," *Rural Opportunities,* II, No. 6 (June, 1967), p. 1.

87. Browning and Northcutt, p. 19.

88. Coles, p. 13.

89. Grower, quoted by Moore, p. 113.

90. Delgado, et al., p. 353.

91. Delgado, et al., p. 353.

92. Delgado, et al., p. 354.

93. Shafer, et al., p. 270.

94. Tumin, p. 41.

95. Coles, p. 21.

96. Delgado, et al., p. 353.

97. "1966 Annual Report," p. 20.

98. "1966 Annual Report," pp. 20–21.

99. Browning and Northcutt, p. 29.

100. Browning and Northcutt, pp. 30–31.

101. Coles, p. 11.

102. *Children in Migrant Families,* p. 43.

103. *Children in Migrant Families,* p. 10.

104. Browning and Northcutt, p. 36.

105. Coles, pp. 21–22.

106. *Children in Migrant Families,* p. 6.

107. Laura Dittmann, *Children in Day Care* (United States Children's Bureau, 1967), p. 105.

108. Moore, p. 117.

109. Shafer, et al., p. 470.

110. *Children in Migrant Families,* p. 12.

111. Dittmann, p. 109.

112. Dittmann, p. 110.

113. *Children in Migrant Families,* p. 25.

114. *These Are Our Children* (New Jersey Summer School Program for Children of Migrant Farm Workers, Department of Education, 1966), p. 4.

115. *These Are Our Children,* p. 9.

116. *Children in Migrant Families,* p. 26.

117. Greene, pp. 8–9.

118. Edgar G. Johnston, "The Education of Children of Spanish-Speaking Migrants in Michigan," *Michigan Academy of Science, Arts and Letters,* XXXII (1946), in Greene, p. 83.

119. A. A. Warburton, H. Wood, and M. M. Crane, *The Work and Welfare of Children of Agricultural Laborers in Hidalgo County, Texas* (Washington: U. S. Government Printing Office, 1943).

120. "Education of Children of Migratory Agricultural Workers," United States Office of Education, in *Children in Migrant Families,* p. 2.

121. "Education on the Move," report of a 1960 Demonstration Summer School for Migrant Children in Manitowoc County, Wisconsin, p. 13.

122. Greene, p. 128.

123. *Children in Migrant Families,* p. 10.

124. Greene, p. 57.

125. Greene, p. 8.

126. Greene, pp. 52–53.

127. Tumin, p. 39.

128. "Senate Labor Unit Rejects an Amendment on Children," *The New York Times* (August 11, 1966).

129. Editorial, "Inching Toward Adequacy," *The New York Times* (September 25, 1966).

130. Greene, p. 73.

131. Greene, p. 8.

132. Tumin, p. 43.

133. Greene, p. 148.

134. Elizabeth Sutton, *Knowing and Teaching the Migrant Child* (Washington, 1960), p. 26.

135. Mildred B. Kantor, "Some Consequences of Residential and Social Mobility for the Adjustment of Children," *Mobility and Mental Health,* ed. Mildred B. Kantor, pp. 87, 108.

136. Sutton, p. 15.

137. Wright, p. 40.

138. Dittmann, p. 111.

139. Coles, p. 14.

140. Sutton, p. 28.

141. Greene, p. 119.

142. Greene, pp. 50, 112.

143. Browning and Northcutt, p. 8.

144. Browning and Northcutt, p. 6.

145. Daniel P. Moynihan, *The Negro Family, The Case for National Action* (Washington: U. S. Government Printing Office, 1965), p. 36.

146. Coles, p. 12.

147. Coles, p. 11.

148. Coles, p. 16.

149. Coles, p. 18.

150. Coles, p. 16.

151. Robert Coles, "What Migrant Farm Children Learn," *Saturday Review* (May 15, 1965), p. 88. Hereafter referred to as Coles, "Children."

152. Coles, "Children," p. 89.

153. Coles, "Children," pp. 74, 88.

154. Coles, "Children," p. 89.

155. Visit by author to school, Woodstown, New Jersey, July, 1966.

156. Tumin, p. 25.

157. Melissa B. Ingling, *Report of the Demonstration Schools for Migrant Children* (Department of Labor and Industry, Bureau of Migrant Labor, Trenton, 1956), in Tumin, p. 25.

158. Tumin, p. 26.

159. Tumin, p. 34.

160. Tumin, p. 47.

161. Visit by author to Indian Mills, New Jersey, July, 1966.

162. Visits by author to Cedarville and Cranbury, New Jersey, July, 1966.

163. *These Are Our Children,* p. 3.
164. *These Are Our Children,* pp. 6–7.
165. Tumin, p. 12.
166. Tumin, p. 28.
167. Tumin, p. 12.
168. Tumin, p. 12.
169. Tumin, p. 13.
170. Tumin, p. 57.
171. Tumin, p. 16.
172. Tumin, p. 17.
173. Tumin, p. 20.
174. Visit by author to Rosenhayn, New Jersey, August, 1966.
175. Bagdikian, p. 92.
176. "Report of Regional Conferences on Education of Migrant Children," U. S. Office of Education, p. 1.
177. Dittmann, p. 112.
178. Coles, "The Migrant Farmer," p. 31.
179. Steinbeck, p. 173.

Index

Watson, Goodwin, quoted on
    schools, 99
Watts, 133–4
Watts, Dorothy D., 159
Weinerman, Dr. E. Richard,
    155
Welfare: 165f; criticism of,
    166; analogy to m. r., 168;
    failure of, 168; lack of
    long-range view, 168–71;
    perpetuation of poverty,
    170–1, 176; categories, 173;
    see also Aid to Dependent
    Children

Well-Child Conference, 65
Williams, Senator Harrison,
    234, 241–2
Wright, Dale, 223; quoted,
    233
Wright, Judge Skelly, quoted
    on tracking, 106

Yerby, Dr. Alonzo S., quoted
    on sickness among poor,
    130–1; 148, 153, 155,
    163–4

ABOUT THE AUTHOR

RODGER HURLEY was born in New York City in 1940. He was educated at Brown University, and after serving with the Special Forces in Vietnam, he earned an M.A. in political science at the Eagleton Institute of Politics, Rutgers University. In 1967 he became a project director for the New Jersey Division of Mental Retardation. At present he is director of a research group appointed by the President's Committee on Mental Retardation to write a report on the effect of hunger and malnutrition on the development of children.

VINTAGE POLITICAL SCIENCE
AND SOCIAL CRITICISM